Which the Justice, Which the Thief

A man may see how this world goes with no eyes. Look with thine ears: see how yond justice rails upon yond simple thief. Hark, in thine ear: change places and, handy-dandy, which is the justice, which is the thief?

—KING LEAR

Which the Justice,
Which the Thief

William Harrington

THE **BOBBS-MERRILL** COMPANY, INC.
A SUBSIDIARY OF HOWARD W. SAMS & CO., INC.
Publishers • INDIANAPOLIS • NEW YORK

LIBRARY OF CONGRESS CATALOG CARD NUMBER 63-18292
COPYRIGHT © 1963 BY WILLIAM HARRINGTON
ALL RIGHTS RESERVED

First printing, 1963

c.\

Printed in the United States of America

"A good parson once said, that where mystery begins religion ends. Cannot I say, as truly at least, of human laws,
that where mystery begins, justice ends?"

—EDMUND BURKE, *A Vindication of
Natural Society*

"And he looked for justice, but, behold, oppression; for
righteousness, but, behold, a cry."

—ISAIAH 5:7.

Which the Justice, Which the Thief

Prologue

WHEN A MAN *lives to be ninety-two years old, people expect him to be a character, and no matter what he does they are going to think he is and laugh over him and repeat his words and point at him. It is a temptation for him to become what they think he should be and so have a little fun out of it. I have been tempted but I hope I have resisted the temptation successfully. I hope I have and I think I have, but I suppose most of the people of Marshall County, Ohio, think I am a character anyway, simply because I have lived so long that my longevity itself is an impropriety.*

My name is William Henry Harrison Applegate, and I have been known as Attorney William H. H. Applegate because that was what I had painted on my office windows for many years. I have been known as Judge Applegate because I was judge of the Court of Common Pleas of Marshall County for an even fifty years, but I insist that the current generation call me Bill, which is what I like to be called and did like to be called outside of the courtroom even when I was a crusty old judge. And I did grow old in office, I must admit. I should have retired ten years sooner, and would have, too, but in these small towns it is difficult to replace a judge. The prosperous lawyers don't want to give up their practices for the bench. So I stayed on and set some kind of record, and whether I was a good judge or not has unfortunately been obscured by the single fact that I was a judge for a very long time.

I have an office in the courthouse. When Henry Kemp succeeded me on the bench he insisted I keep the office I had had for fifty years, and that favor I was glad to accept. So he ousted the bailiff, who really has no need for a room anyway, and I still come to my old office daily and sit behind my desk and read my newspaper, and Judge Kemp and the lawyers around town come in to talk to me and consult about their cases, and they are very kind. Now, according to the rules of being ninety-two years old, I should wear white suits and walk to my office every morning, carrying a cane. In fact, my housekeeper, Mary Gillian, drives me downtown and comes to pick me up, and I never owned a white suit in my life.

Well, what is the difference? To whom am I telling all this and why? People said, "Write your memoirs, write about the cases you tried during all those years." But I don't like old people who reminisce. I never did, and I have determined not to be one. Besides, the one distinct impression I carry about being a judge year after year is that it was dull. I presided over many trials, and some were important, and some were interesting, but I cannot see that posterity will suffer if they are unrecorded. I did like the idea of writing a book, however. It is supposed to gratify the ego to contemplate posterity reading some words of yours preserved between two covers on library shelves. But what can I write about? Only about trials, because trials are all I really know. And the most interesting trial I ever saw in the Marshall County courthouse occurred only last year. Perhaps I think it was the most interesting only because it is recent and so is more vividly impressed on my memory. I am not yet senile, and I still remember recent events better than I do remote ones. I decided to write this book, and if I live to finish it—I see no reason why I should not, since I feel as healthy now as I have in the past sixty years—then perhaps readers will find some interest in an old *judge's observations of a twentieth-century criminal trial in this most free of nations.*

I am not a prodigy of memory. I asked the reporter to type up a transcript. I talked to the attorneys. Even so, I may not understand the trial as well as I think I do, and not everyone will agree with my judgment of the testimony and the events.

I

IF I BELIEVE in one thing—reader, forgive me, for I am going
to impose my ideas on you from time to time since this is after
all my book—it is economy of words. I have read too many long
briefs. So I will be abrupt and without further comment say that
I intend to write about a case of armed robbery, that it involved
two accused defendants, and that it was called *State of Ohio vs.
Roger Louis* and *State of Ohio vs. Ruth Gibson.* They were
accused of robbing the DeWitt Jewelry Store in Alexandria at
gunpoint and escaping with $201.84 and a paper bag full of
watches and rings.

The case was tried in the September term of court, which
meant that it came up for trial on Tuesday, October 17, 1961.

Our courthouse in Alexandria—the county seat of Marshall
County, named not for the ancient city of Egypt but in honor
of Alexander Hamilton, the name Hamilton having been ap-
propriated far to the west of us before our forefathers could
claim it—is a brick structure built right after the Civil War. It
contains all the county offices, except the prosecuting attorney's,

13

and it was built for appearance, not for efficiency or even for economy. Inevitably it has its clock tower, and inevitably the clock strikes the hours not quite accurately. The clock has four faces, and no two of them ever precisely agree. Thus when it is nine o'clock to the south of the courthouse it is a minute past to the north but four minutes before to the east and two minutes before to the west. It is a matter of no great moment, however, especially in the summer when the trees are in leaf and you cannot see the clock from the streets below, except from certain spots where you can see through. The courthouse is a red brick building, with white wooden trim, and the clock tower is white and built of wood. It sits on a square, and the traffic on the town's main streets circulates around the square. Behind the courthouse is another building on the square, called the annex. It is newer, having been built about 1925; and it contains the sheriff's office and apartment, the jail, and a small garage for the county cars. People who haven't seen many small towns think the arrangement is charming. I suppose it is, but if the county ever had the money we would make it a whole lot less charming.

The courtroom is unnecessarily big and occupies a major share of the space in the courthouse. When the courthouse was built the country people came in from the hills during the court sessions, and it was a sort of festival and something of a civic duty to sit in the courtroom and watch the lawyers perform; but I do not recall seeing the courtroom filled with people more than five or six times in all the years I was judge. Nevertheless it gives justice a sort of awesome dignity which it otherwise unfortunately lacks to hold court in a big courtroom, and I have always been glad that the builders of the Marshall County courthouse thought it necessary to build the courtroom much larger than efficiency or economy would have dictated. The courtroom is old now, and a bit dilapidated. But even its age contributes to the air of the place. It is like justice itself, not modern, not streamlined or efficient, but ponderous and antique with its worn spots showing and its loose threads dangling, experienced and changed by experience, and perfectly suited to the job it is supposed to perform. The room is not paneled but plastered, and the plaster is painted buff. The woodwork, the door and window frames and the baseboard are of dark oak. The carpet is maroon and thread-bare. The lights are milky glass globes with bulbs in them. The furniture is heavy dark oak with black leather and brass studs, and some of it is scarred. Behind the bar the public benches look like church pews and are devilishly uncomfortable, which keeps out the loafers. To the right of the bench an elevated table sits on a little platform one step up. This is for the clerk, but there are two chairs at that table, and it is understood that one of those armchairs is mine. There I sit and watch the trials. The office which is mine but should be the judge's opens immediately behind that elevated table, and I can sit in my office with the door open and hear the trials and come in when I want to.

This particular trial began, as I said, on October seventeenth. Trials begin at nine o'clock, and by eight-thirty I was in my office, and shortly after I went out and took my chair in the court-room. Henry Kemp—he is the judge, of course—had met me on the steps of the courthouse that morning and accompanied me to my office. Henry suffers a little stage fright when a trial is about to start. He was a good lawyer, Henry; better than the practice he had would have indicated, but he was a book lawyer. By that I mean that he was never a man to give an offhand opinion without first checking in a book. He gave the impression that he knew very little law at all, knew only where to find it. That was not so; really he was only cautious. As a judge he has to rule from the bench, and that disturbs him. Give him a few minutes to check his law and a few minutes more to ponder, and Henry is confident and not often wrong; but make him rule quickly on a point of evidence, and he is not confident but he still is not often wrong. Henry was glad enough to become a judge, although tak-ing a judgeship in a community like this amounts almost to a confession that a man has not attained the first rank as a prac-ticing lawyer. It pays about $10,000 a year now, and the judge does not have to strain himself to earn his pay, but if his practice is good, he can double that perhaps, or with a little less luck not double it but still exceed it considerably, and so a lawyer with a flourishing practice does not ordinarily want to become a judge if his health is good. When I first ran for the office, I did it be-cause *I* was not earning as much money as I wanted and the opening was there. In Henry Kemp's case, a similar motive moved him. He is in his forties, and he was not an eminently successful attorney. He had his clients, but the good practice always eluded him. Two or three men tend to monopolize the banks, the insurance companies, and the good estates, and Henry never was able to break in. He had his divorces and his collections and his adoptions and guardianships, his deeds and leases, his little businesses, a few tax returns and an occasional negligence trial always as counsel for the plaintiff, and once in a very long while he defended a criminal. He was making a comfortable living but he had to work hard at it, and he had to put up with a lot of nasty people. When he agreed to run for the unexpired term I had decided to leave, Henry abandoned whatever ambition he had to break into the exclusive circle of the best-fixed attorneys. The bar welcomed Henry's decision to take the judgeship, and if no maverick loses his head and decides to run against him, he will never have an opponent. I had opposition only twice in all my years. Filling the judgeships in a small town is often embarrassing for the lawyers. They want a capable man on the bench, someone who will give them fair decisions and not make too many mistakes—someone who will not embarrass them when occasionally out-of-town counsel comes in to work in their courtroom—it is a point of honor with them—and yet they do not want to run for the office themselves. They are glad, therefore, when a Henry Kemp will take the office. He does credit to their bar. It removes him from competition among them. It is a satisfactory arrangement all around. They are fortunate to have him on the bench and they know it.

Henry was a little nervous that morning, as I said, and he wanted to talk. He did not have a chance to talk much. Knowing that he would be in trial all day, three attorneys came in early with journal entries for him to sign, and he had to go to his office to take care of that, and I was left alone in my seat. I had my newspaper, the Columbus paper I receive every morning and read from force of habit, but I was given no opportunity to read it. The bailiff came up to say good morning. Quentin Strickland is our bailiff—can you imagine a bailiff with a name like that in a small-town common pleas court? Quentin was my bailiff for eleven years or so. He got his job as a political favor to his father, who was Republican chairman a few years ago. His father is not chairman any more, but what can you do with a fellow like Quentin? He does a good job, isn't paid much, and to lose his job would be a tragedy for him. So we keep him on and suffer his limitation; for he is not too bright. I should not perhaps go that far. He is not mentally retarded, but he has never been the man his father wanted him to be. His worst fault from my point of view is that his vision and his imagination are bounded absolutely within the limits of small-town life. He never wanted to live anywhere but in Alexandria and never wanted anything not available here.

"Good morning, Judge," he said to me when he came into the courtroom. Quentin is bald, fifty years old, slight of stature. He wears double-breasted suits, whether they are in style or not, and bow ties and gold-rimmed round spectacles. He is meticulous and dutiful and takes his work very seriously.

"Good morning, Quentin," I answered.

He walked across the room to me, saying, "Going to be a big trial, isn't it?" When I did not comment he went on and said, "Joe'll put the hooks into that pair, Judge. He's got enough on them to hang 'em. He'll put the hooks into them, all right."

Again I made no reply, and I suppose he decided I did not want to talk to him. He walked away. My next visitor was Bill Mullen, a tall, skinny young man who writes for the Alexandria *Intelligencer*. I always want to cut his hair for him. Aside from that, I like Bill Mullen, except that he writes about the court without having the vaguest notion of what is happening. It makes no difference, because if he reported accurately his employers wouldn't publish it anyway. They want what they call human interest in their stories, which means they want them written to sell newspapers and not so they will report what really happens.

"Good morning, Judge," Bill Mullen said to me, and he stepped up on the platform and took the chair beside me. When the clerk does not want his chair, which is most of the time, Bill sits there and takes his notes. He is usually the only newspaper reporter in our courtroom. When others come they must take their seats behind the bar.

"There's quite a collection of witnesses checking in out there," he said. "Do you want to make a guess on this trial?"

"I have a long-standing habit of maintaining an open mind," I said.

"The proper judicial attitude," he said. "I wouldn't be surprised," he went on, changing the subject, "if some other papers show up today. This one's kind of interesting."

"I suppose it is," I said. "We're going to have a crowd."

People were coming in and taking seats on the benches in the back of the courtroom. A few of them are what I always called regulars, a dozen or so retired or chronically unemployed men who loaf about the streets and always come in for any mildly interesting trial. They always sit together in the last row, where they can get out to go to the men's room frequently. Then some country people came in hesitantly, looking around, and they stood awhile before sitting down, as though expecting someone to tell them to leave. The men were dressed in clean work pants and wool shirts, except for one or two who wore suits for the occasion and were manifestly uncomfortable, and the women wore print dresses and low-heeled shoes with white socks. These were hill families, like the ones who live across the river in West Virginia, but they were not immigrants from the Mountain State; they had lived in these southern Ohio hills for generations, independent people and ignorant, most of them. They have very little nobility, though they themselves are aware of the lore that says they do. They grub at the land to make their living, and they have been indoctrinated, perhaps by their Granges, with the notion that being farmers makes them superior to the rest of mankind. They think they are more honest than other people, and many of them are, though as a class they have more than their share of dishonest men and women among them. They think no law applies to them unless it says specifically that it applies to farmers. I exaggerate, of course, but generations of experience with special government farm plans has ingrained some such notion. They are all marginal farmers, and the more ambitious among them leave the hills for the cities and work in factories and buy cheap cars and drive home to the hills every weekend.

They are at once aggressive and timid, independent and slavish, honest and dishonest—what they are on a given occasion depends on what you have to do with one of them. One thing they do for certain is vote. They are politically conscious. Woe unto the county official who offends them. They do not forgive. They are easily awed, as they were this day in the courtroom, but in their element they are assertive. I have never liked them as a class, though I have known many fine people among them. You can hardly help sympathizing with the grizzled patriarch of one of their families, sitting in your office in his brand new bib overalls, scrubbed clean but with a stubble of gray beard on his chin, humble and amiable and expressing to you in a quiet and ungrammatical way some idea you may disagree with but to which you give respectful audience because you understand the limitations of its source and do not wish to offend. On the other hand when you remember that he and his kind will assert this same idea in the community and have the numbers to make it stick, then he and his quaint idea take on a totally different aspect, because you know that these people and these ideas stifle the community by stifling progress. They are Republicans, these people, almost to a man, and will support and vote for the Republican candidates on all but the local level, no matter who those candidates are and what they have done. They form a bloc which petrifies the party by relieving it of the need to fight for its support. They elected me year after year without suspecting what I really thought of them.

"Do you recognize the Louises or the Gibsons?" I asked Bill Mullen.

"No," he said. "I don't."

"Well," I told him, "I see two or three Louises back there, but which ones claim this boy I don't know. They're a clan, of course. They'll be in the courtroom, all of them who can get here. Some of them will come to gloat over the boy's being in trouble. They don't like each other much."

"They won't like the Gibsons either," Bill said.

"No. That name doesn't mean much to me. I can't remember any Gibsons around, but I suppose there must be some."

19

"I haven't looked into the families," Bill said. "You know Charley. He won't publish anything until we're ready to go. He'll want it now, though."

Several of the country people nodded greetings to me, and two of them ventured up to the bar to speak. I spoke to them and asked them how they were. They like me. I am a legend to them. That is a responsibility I did not invite.

The first attorney to arrive in the courtroom was Bob Day, who was appointed by the court to defend Ruth Gibson. Neither she nor her family had the money to pay a defense attorney, so Henry appointed Bob. He would get $100 from the county for the defense. He has been in practice here by himself for two years. He can do that because his family has enough money to keep him going for the first five years. The day when a young man could hang out a shingle and be in business has just about disappeared. He won't make a living in most communities today, not for five years, and maybe more. So most of them go into firms, or take jobs with salaries and security. It is fashionable in some circles to say what a shame that is, how it reflects a lack of independence or character or something or other on the part of our young people. That's malarkey. It reflects the changing conditions of life. Anyway, the Days have the money. I imagine Bob himself has a nice chunk of stock paying him dividends, and I know he inherited the house he lives in and so has evaded that major expense. He is a solid young fellow, turning bald already though not yet thirty. He has a cute little wife and two daughters. In court he wore a dark blue suit, black tie and a white shirt, and he looked good, I thought. He brought to court a manila folder enclosing a copy of the indictment and a few other papers, as well as a yellow legal pad on which to take notes, but no briefcase.

Judge Kemp usually appoints two or three of the younger attorneys to handle all the defenses the county has to pay for. The older lawyers call that policy Henry Kemp's emancipation proclamation. When I was judge I appointed each lawyer in turn, alphabetically. One or two of these pasty-white bankers' lawyers simply blanched to have to defend nasty criminals, but I regarded these appointive defenses as a corporate obligation of the entire bar and I insisted that every lawyer bear his share of that burden. I did let them pay the younger men to do it for them if they wanted to, but the fee had to be reasonable; I would not stand for their just handing over the $100. Henry Kemp looks at it differently. He thinks it is good experience for the young men and helps them establish their reputations. The trouble is, most of these cases are impossible to win, and the young fellows get a reputation for losing. Also, I think that the indigent defendant who has to be defended at public expense has a right to experienced counsel. There is room for difference of opinion on the subject. In any event, I do not mention all this to be critical of Bob Day. Far from it.

The next attorney to come in was John Kimball MacInroth—he likes to use his full name—defense counsel for the Louis boy. Now MacInroth's services are expensive, so the Louis family must have paid him well just to retain him. By reputation, no lawyer in Marshall County can quite approach MacInroth. He is no quiet bankers' lawyer. He has the loud practice—the messy divorces, the big automobile accident claims, and a major portion of the criminal cases where the defendants can afford to pay. His reputation also includes a notion that he verges on the shyster, although I never caught him in the slightest impropriety in my court. It is said that to retain MacInroth is almost a confession of guilt, because only someone in deep trouble could afford him. This idea has not prevented him from winning a remarkably high percentage of his cases.

MacInroth is a personality, of course, with a big smile and many handshakes for everyone as he comes into a courtroom, and he was himself as the trial started. He has a shock of white hair, contrasting nicely with a ruddy complexion. He dresses somewhat ostentatiously. He drives a Cadillac. He took his seat beside Bob Day at the defense table after asking Day to move over and let him have the seat he wanted. He got up and came over to say good morning to me, and then he sat down again.

MacInroth is not a native of these hills. I cannot remember where he comes from, though I have heard someone say. He had hard times when he first settled in Alexandria. People did not trust him, did not like him. He served two terms as township clerk and then two terms as city solicitor to earn a little money and establish his name in the community. He won a few hard cases and he was on his way. He wanted the bank and insurance business, the good retainers, the big estates, but he could not get them. People said he would steal, which was not true. Since he was unable to get that kind of practice he had to concentrate on the sort of cases at which he became an expert, and in time he was making more money than attorneys he had once envied. MacInroth is an example of a man who carved a niche for himself, as the phrase is. I am old enough to remember this.

Then Roger Louis came in. Louis was a young fellow, twenty-seven years old, of average height and rather thin; he had an olive complexion, and dark hair which he could not control. He looked dirty, in a way, but he wasn't. Some people have an unwashed look, no matter how washed they are; I don't know how you can overcome it. Louis was one of those people, and it was too bad for him. He came into the courtroom with his father, nodding his acknowledgment of some words his father spoke before they separated, and he came forward through the swinging gate in the bar in response to MacInroth's gesture. Louis was dressed in blue trousers and a checkered gray sport coat and a shiny red tie. He knew people were looking at him, and he did not like it. He was nervous. Who wouldn't be, considering? He was facing a possible twenty-five years' imprisonment. He sat down beside MacInroth; MacInroth spoke briefly to him and then turned back to a conference he was having with Bob Day.

Then Ruth Gibson was brought in. I say brought in because the Gibsons had not been able to raise bond for her, and she had been in jail all summer. The sheriff's wife brought Ruth into the courtroom and escorted her to her seat beside Bob Day and at the opposite end of the table from Roger Louis. She did not speak to Louis or to MacInroth. Ruth Gibson was a dark-haired, dark-eyed, rather pretty girl of twenty-two, wearing a tailored gray suit with much padding in the shoulders, a light-blue blouse, and flat shoes. She had on no makeup. Nearly everyone in the courtroom was still colored in October by the summer sun we had all experienced, but Ruth had been in the county jail all summer, and she looked white by contrast with other people.

She really looked pitiable. I am not sure whether her lawyer had told her to put on this look or whether it was the natural product of her circumstances. Probably it was a combination of both. I remember seeing her around town before her arrest; she had not looked so pitiful then, though I remembered her as a shy country girl working as a waitress. This day she faced the same possibility as Roger Louis—twenty-five years' imprisonment; but she appeared much calmer than he. She did not look around the courtroom at the people staring at her. Bob Day went on talking to MacInroth, and Ruth listened to their conversation, keeping her eyes fixed in their direction.

Quentin brought the jury panel in and placed them by number in the jury box. The extra members of the panel were seated in chairs inside the bar. Jim Schneider, the investigator from the prosecutor's office, came in and placed a cardboard carton on the floor beside the prosecution table. Ruth Gibson looked up at Jim, her eyes moving after him. She did not like him. He had interrogated her. The box caused some excitement in Louis, and he leaned across to MacInroth to comment about it.

Judge Henry Kemp came in the door at the side and took two steps into the courtroom before he turned back to say a parting word to someone in the clerk's office, then finally walked to the bench and took his seat. The two attorneys, no one else, rose momentarily, but Henry with a motion put them back in their seats. One of the girls from the clerk's office came out and put a file before Henry; he sent her out to get him a book, and she returned with that. Henry looked at his wrist watch, then turned and looked at the clock over the jury box. It was two minutes after nine. He opened his book to a marked page and spread out the papers from his file. I might note at this point that judges in our court do not wear robes. My predecessor did, more than fifty years ago, and I did for a few years at first, but the robes are too hot in the summer, and expensive, so I gave them up. Very few common pleas judges of my acquaintance wear them any more. I suppose we have laid aside our dignity. At least those of us have who depended on the robes for dignity.

We were ready for the trial, but we didn't have a prosecutor. Joe Baumgardner would not have been late when I was judge.

I used to charge the lawyers ten dollars a minute for contempt when they were late. Henry Kemp has let things slide to that extent. Anyway, Joe came in four minutes late and in a hurry as always, carrying a file with loose papers sticking out at both ends. He spoke a quick word of apology to the judge before he sat down.

"*State of Ohio versus Louis* and *State of Ohio versus Gibson,*" said the judge, and the reporter began to take the record on the little machine on her table. The trial had begun.

"You're ready?" the judge asked, and each of the attorneys said he was.

"All those who are here for jury duty will rise," said the judge in a voice loud enough to be heard throughout the courtroom. The people knew the trial had begun then, and some of them who were still talking stopped and turned their attention to the proceedings.

With the prospective jurors standing, the clerk stepped forward and administered to them their oath to tell the truth during the *voir dire.* When they were seated, the judge nodded to Joe Baumgardner.

Joe stood up. I might say of Joe Baumgardner that he was a portly, distinguished-looking man, some fifty years old. He was probate judge for two terms and then resigned to reopen his private practice. He ran for prosecutor to secure an income while he rebuilt his practice. In counties the size of ours, the job of prosecutor is not a full-time job by any means. It takes perhaps half a man's time. The prosecutor keeps his own office and moves the county's files in where he can find room for them. A secretary and an investigator go with the job, and it pays about $5,000 a year. Joe had been prosecutor about three years at this time. He came from one of those German families that are so numerous in these Ohio towns. They used to form a community all their own. I can remember when there was a German-language newspaper published in Marshall County, the old *Zeitung;* it ceased publication at the time of the First World War. The German families spoke German in their homes even after they had been here two or three generations. Besides their newspaper, they had their old-fashioned beer parlors and a couple of the finest restaurants I have ever eaten in anywhere. The Baumgardners —once spelled Baumgartner, I think—were farmers. They had a nice spread in the flat bottom land along the river, and I can remember Joe's grandfather, who wore a long beard almost down to his waist. They used to entertain everyone of importance in Alexandria every summer at the farmhouse, the big white farmhouse where they had a grand piano shipped in all the way from Berlin, and Joe's grandmother would play and sing for the guests. They made ice cream by the gallon, out of real cream, always vanilla, and German pastries enough to load the long tables they set up on the lawn; the guests would go away at the end of the evening simply gorged with rich food. Joe had that German corpulence we always identified with the Baumgardners. The farm is gone now, sold off in pieces, and most of the family has moved away.

Joe spoke to the jurors in general. "Now, ladies and gentlemen, you have all served as jurors before during this trial term, and you know what we are going to do. I will ask a few general questions, and if anyone can answer yes to any question, he should raise his hand. Okay?

"In the first place, I am Joseph Baumgardner, Prosecuting Attorney of Marshall County. I practice law, and my office is in the City Bank Building. Is anyone here currently a client of mine? No? All right, then; the attorney for the defense of Mr. Louis is Mr. John MacInroth, and he is a lawyer with offices in the same building, and he practices law with his partner, Mr. Fischer, and they call their firm MacInroth and Fischer. Does anyone have any business in their office right now?"

Two hands were raised, one by juror number four, and one by juror number seventeen, who was seated in a chair outside the jury box.

"Mr. Reece," said Joe to juror number four. "What do you have in Mr. MacInroth's office?"

"He's my wife's lawyer, and she's divorcing me," said Reece in a sort of ironic tone. There was laughter in the courtroom, including some by MacInroth.

"Would that tend to influence your view of the case?" asked Joe smoothly and somewhat facetiously.

"He'll be excused," said Judge Kemp.

Reece rose and left the jury box, and juror number thirteen moved in to take his place.

Joe turned to juror number seventeen. "Mrs. Ross, is that right?" he asked. The woman nodded. "What do you have in Mr. MacInroth's office?"

"He's handling my father-in-law's estate," said the woman.

Joe nodded and made a checkmark by her name on his jury list. "Is anyone else represented in any way by the firm of Mac-Inroth and Fischer?" he asked, and when no one raised a hand he went on. "Now, the attorney for Miss Gibson is Mr. Robert Day, a young lawyer who practices law at four twenty-six Maple Street. Is anyone currently doing business with his office?"

Juror number eleven spoke up and said, "He sent me a collection letter once. I didn't owe it."

There was some laughter again, and Joe said, "Would that tend in any way at all to prejudice you for or against Mr. Day's client?"

"No," said the juror positively.

"Anyone else?" asked Joe. "All right. Now is anyone in any way related to any of these attorneys or their wives? No? Is anyone a close friend of any of them?"

"Well, I know you pretty well, Joe," said juror number one.

"Sure you do, Linnie," Joe said. "Would that influence your decision in any way?"

"No, I don't think so. I can be fair about it."

"Okay, anyone else? No? Is anyone on the jury in any way related to either Mr. Roger Louis or Miss Ruth Gibson? Is anyone a close friend of either of them or any of their families? No? Okay. Now one of the witnesses in this case will be a young man by the name of Paul Russell, known usually as Doc Russell. Is anyone related to him or does anyone consider himself a close friend of his?"

Three jurors acknowledged that they knew Russell, but they denied that would influence their decision.

"Now, ladies and gentlemen," Joe said, moving over toward the jury box, "we are going to try a criminal case, and if one or both of these defendants is found guilty it may result in the

26

imprisonment of one or both of them. Is there anyone on the jury who would not vote to find a person guilty, even knowing he was guilty, because of some moral conviction about imprisoning people?"

No one responded. I would not allow that question when I was judge.

"Now," Joe went on, "you will be charged as a matter of law that you shall not find a defendant guilty unless guilt is proved beyond a reasonable doubt. Is there anyone here who would not vote guilty if guilt were proved beyond a reasonable doubt? In other words, is there anyone here who could not accept that idea, reasonable doubt, who would expect the state to remove all possible doubt, real or imaginary?"

It was not really a question; it was argument, and never in my years on the bench did I see a juror respond to that question.

Judge Kemp nodded to MacInroth, who rose and walked across the front of the courtroom and leaned against the rail of the jury box.

To the juror nearest him, juror number six, he said, "Mrs. Teitelbaum, you won't mind answering a few questions for me, will you? We've done this before."

It was true, of course, that the two had been through it before. This was the sixth trial of the term, and each of the five preceding juries had been chosen from the same array. Some of these people had been on all five. We have to use the same jurors. It would be impracticable to draw a new array of jurors for every trial. Yet I have had my doubts, as I suppose every judge and lawyer has, about trying case after case before the same jury. Sometimes I think that they do better justice the first time they serve than they do the fifth or sixth time. Jurors become sophisticated with experience, or think they do. They think they can guess the lawyers' motives, guess what the lawyers are hiding, and anticipate lawyers' speeches. Also, they learn to like some lawyers and to dislike others, and I am afraid this sentiment may influence their decisions. This was the fourth criminal trial of the term, so Joe Baumgardner was appearing before them for the fourth time. He had won three convictions from them. It was the second trial before them for MacInroth.

Mrs. Teitelbaum smiled and nodded. She was happy to be a juror. Few Jewish families live in the county. They have no problem whatever about prejudice, not that I ever detected, anyway; nevertheless I think it pleased Mrs. Teitelbaum, and probably her whole family, that she was called on to participate in public affairs. She was a conscientious juror. Maybe she wanted to prove what a good citizen a Jew can be. I don't think she needed to prove any such thing, but maybe she thought she did.

"Mrs. Teitelbaum," said MacInroth, "do you know who owns the DeWitt Jewelry Company?"

"Yes, it is owned by Mr. Nathan Garfield," she replied. Her family had lived in Marshall County for half a century or so. The older ones spoke with an accent. Her generation speaks English so well that the perfection is an accent.

"Are you acquainted with Mr. Garfield?"

"Mr. Garfield and my husband have a business relationship, and we are acquainted."

"What is the nature of that business relationship?"

"Mr. Garfield buys his automobiles from our agency."

"You do a lot of business with him?"

"He buys a new car every other year or so."

"Mrs. Teitelbaum," said MacInroth, "Mr. Garfield may be a witness for the prosecution. Would you be more inclined to believe his word than, let us say, the word of Roger Louis because of your acquaintance?"

"Well," she said, "I know Mr. Garfield as an honest man."

"You also said, I believe, that you know his employee, Doc Russell. How well do you know him?"

"He has waited on me in the store, that's all."

"If this case reduced itself to a matter of taking his word against someone else's word, would you be influenced by your acquaintance with him or with Mr. Garfield, his employer?"

"No, I am sure I wouldn't."

"You are sure?"

"Yes."

MacInroth smiled the smile that lawyers reserve for jurors

and said, "All right, Mrs. Teitelbaum, thank you." Then he moved to the next juror, number five. "Mr. Cleveland," he said, "can you think of any reason why you could not render an impartial verdict between these two defendants and the State of Ohio?"

"Nope," said the juror casually, shaking his head. He was a hill farmer, dressed in a double-breasted gray suit and a blue and gray wool shirt with a blue necktie. He sat easily in the jury box with his legs crossed. He was deeply tanned and deeply wrinkled, and his plentiful hair was white and neatly parted.

"You're a farmer, I think you told me before," said MacInroth.

"Man and boy," confirmed Mr. Cleveland.

"Ever buy anything at DeWitt's?"

"Never did."

"Okay, thank you, Mr. Cleveland," said MacInroth, and he moved down the box to talk to juror number thirteen, who had been placed in the seat of juror number four after Mr. Reece was excused. "Hello, Miss O'Hara," he said. "Another day of jury duty." Miss O'Hara nodded. "No reason why you shouldn't be a juror, is there?"

"I suppose not," she said. She was a small red-headed woman of about thirty, a clerk in the local Woolworth dimery.

"You know Doc Russell, don't you?"

"I know him," she said. Her voice if not her words implied that she did not like Doc Russell.

"Is your acquaintance going to influence you to believe what he says?"

"No."

"Okay. Thank you." MacInroth stepped up to the next seat in the jury box, to juror number three. "Mrs. Goodman," he said. "Is there any reason why you might not be able to take an impartial view of this case?"

"No," she said positively. She was a housewife. Her husband teaches at Alexandria High School. They are about fifty years old, with a son in the Navy.

MacInroth stepped back from the jury box. "I would like to address one further question to everyone," he said. "Some of the testimony in this case is apt to be the testimony of policemen or of deputy sheriffs. Is there anyone here who has the idea that a man ought to be believed more than someone else because he is a policeman or a deputy?"

Juror number eight spoke up and said, "I know some of the boys pretty well."

"Thank you, Mr. Taylor," said MacInroth. "I'll ask you a little more about that when I get to you." Turning back to Mrs. Goodman, he said, "And thank you, Mrs. Goodman." Then he moved to juror number two. "Good morning, Mr. Paccinelli."

"Good morning," said Paccinelli. Several families of Italians live in Marshall County. They have been here since before the First World War. Joe Paccinelli works for the Gulf Oil Company —not in a filling station, but for the local distributor. He is a man forty years old, a practicing Catholic, and the father of four.

"You know the Garfields pretty well, don't you, Joe?" asked MacInroth. "That isn't going to influence you in any way, is it?"

"I wish I could say it was," said Joe Paccinelli. "I'd like to get out of here and go about my business."

"Well," said MacInroth, "if we could get the prosecutor to drop this ridiculous prosecution we could all have a day off."

"Sure," said Joe Paccinelli.

"Meanwhile I'm afraid you make a very acceptable juror."

"Sure."

"Good morning, Linnie," said MacInroth to the next juror, number one.

"Good morning, Mr. MacInroth," said Linnie Gardner. Linnie was fifty-five or sixty. All her adult life she had worked in other people's houses, except for the times when she was pregnant and bearing her children. She would clean, iron, wash, cook, even cater acceptably. Her husband worked steadily, but only for the city street department. Linnie thought she had to supplement their income, and she was right—she did. Jury duty was Linnie's moment in the limelight. She dressed in her best, with a filmy handkerchief fluffed out in her dress pocket, and she leaned forward and grasped the rail of the jury box with knobby, arthritic hands. She smiled enthusiastically at MacInroth, afraid he would find some reason to excuse her.

"Linnie, is there any reason why you can't render an impartial verdict between the State and these defendants?" said MacInroth importantly.

"No, siree," she said, "no reason at all. I can be fair."

"Thank you, Linnie," said he, and when he looked up toward the next juror, Linnie visibly relaxed.

"Good morning, Miss Tubman," said MacInroth to juror number seven. Miss Tubman, I should relate, was a pretty girl of twenty-two years. She lived on a farm out in the country, and was a waitress in a roadhouse. She would have welcomed being excused from jury duty, but Mr. Taylor beside her, juror number eight, would have been unhappy. They had sat together on three other cases, and Taylor was making progress with the pretty Miss Tubman. In fact, they had been seen holding hands once when the jury went out to lunch.

"Hello," she said to MacInroth. Ruth Gibson might have wished she had Linda Tubman's looks and manner.

"Do you know any of the people involved in this case, Miss Tubman?" asked MacInroth.

"I know them all," said Miss Tubman.

"You know them all?"

"Sure, they all come in out at the place where I work, Paradise Inn. I've seen 'em all out there lots of times."

"Together?"

"No. Each one separately."

"Would you say you are well acquainted with any of them?"

"No, I wouldn't know their names if I didn't hear you say who they are here."

"Except Doc Russell. He hasn't been in the courtroom."

"Well, I've seen him several times and know who he is."

"Ever talk to him?"

"I've waited on his table, taken his order for beer."

"Well, now, Miss Tubman, how is all this going to affect your verdict as a juror?"

"Well, I don't know."

"Well, would you be inclined to believe or disbelieve the word of one of these three people because you have seen them in your place of employment and have waited on their table?"

"No," said she with a little shrug.

"You think you could render a fair verdict in this case?"

"Oh, sure. I don't have anything against any of them. Or for them, either."

"All right, thank you. How about you, Mr. Taylor? Is there any reason why you can't render a fair verdict?"

"No, sir," responded Taylor quickly. He works behind the meat counter at the A & P.

"What about this friendship of yours with members of the police force?"

"Well, I just know a couple of the fellows on the force. I play baseball with 'em sometimes."

"Is that going to influence your decision? Would you be inclined to believe a policeman more than someone else?"

"Oh, no," said he, and then he laughed and said, "I've heard some of 'em tell some pretty big lies sometimes. About fish they caught or somethin' like that."

"Have you heard any of the policemen talk about this case?"

"No, sir."

"In fact," said MacInroth, stepping back and speaking out to all the jurors, "is there anyone on the jury who has heard talk about the case? That is, anyone who has heard talk from anyone who really knows anything about it. Your own conversation in the family across the dinner table is not what I have in mind."

No one responded.

"Okay, then. Thank you, Mr. Taylor." MacInroth spoke to juror number nine. "Mr. Nicholas, good morning."

Mr. Nicholas nodded. He was a man of seventy or more. He had been a carpenter but was retired now. He fixed my porch floor for me several times. He was a sloppy carpenter, but he made a living.

The judge spoke: "Mr. Nicholas, you are over seventy years old, are you not?"

"Beg pardon?" said Nicholas.

"You are more than seventy years old, aren't you?"

"Seventy-three," said Nicholas, nodding.

"You are entitled to be excused if you want to be."

"Beg pardon?"

"At your age you don't have to serve if you don't want to."

"I want to," said Mr. Nicholas. "Got nothin' else to do."

"Mr. Nicholas," said MacInroth, "do you think you can render a fair verdict between the State of Ohio and these defendants?"

"Sure," responded Mr. Nicholas.

"Good morning, Ed," said MacInroth to juror number ten, Edward Jocelyn, merchant and proprietor of the Jocelyn Department Store. Jocelyn is a good citizen and considers himself an important fellow, impatient to complete his jury service and yet eager to do his duty properly while he was doing so. "Ed," said MacInroth, "there is no reason why you shouldn't be a juror, is there?"

"I suppose not," said Jocelyn.

"You're a pretty good friend of Nathan Garfield."

"Yes."

"But that's not going to influence you?"

"No."

"No. Thank you. Now, Mr. Martin, how about you? Is there any reason why you can't render a fair verdict?"

"No," said Martin, shaking his head. Martin is a farmer, a man of some forty years. His hill farm could not possibly support his family, so he works in a factory during the day, forty hours a week, and works the farm evenings and weekends. The factory supports him, but even so he calls himself a farmer and will not give up the land.

"Okay, thank you," said MacInroth. Then he looked to the last juror. "Mrs. Ketterman, good morning. Is there any reason why you can't be a juror?"

"Yes, there is," she replied. Mrs. Ketterman is the wife of a pharmacist out in Page, one of the little villages in Marshall County.

"Oh," said MacInroth. "What reason is that?"

"I've made up my mind about the case," she said.

"Oh?" said MacInroth. "How does that happen?"

"Well, my husband and I have talked about it, and I've made up my mind."

The judge interrupted. "Where did you get your information, Mrs. Ketterman?"

"I read about the case in the newspaper," she replied.

"You're a liar, Mrs. Ketterman," said Judge Henry Kemp angrily, and everyone in the courtroom started. "You've said this about three cases now. You're just trying to evade jury duty. You're in contempt. You apparently think you're too important to do the civic duty that all of these other people are here doing. Well, you're not. You're nothing but a petty liar. Well, we won't force you to be a good citizen. You're really not qualified to serve on a jury anyway, not with your attitude. You're excused. You're excused permanently. Don't come back. Next juror, step up, please."

Mrs. Ketterman hustled angrily out of the box and out of the courtroom in the midst of staring silence. Her face was very red. She had much to say, but she was afraid to say anything. Henry Kemp lost a vote or two there if he wants to be re-elected. Of course he won about fifty others.

Juror number fourteen worked her way up to the seat vacated by Mrs. Ketterman. MacInroth consulted his list and said, "Mrs. Devine?" The woman nodded. I knew her. Mrs. Henry Devine is the wife of the cashier in the Butler branch of the City Bank. She is a big fat lady.

"Mrs. Devine," said MacInroth, "you have been listening to the questions I have been asking the other jurors, haven't you? Would you have anything you want to tell us? Any reason why you can't serve?"

"No."

"Not acquainted with any of the people we have been talking about?"

"No."

"Mrs. Devine, you are the sister of Henry Nelson, aren't you?"

"That's right."

"Nelson's Garage?"

"That's right."

"Let's see. Henry Nelson was held up a few years ago, wasn't he?"

"Yes, he had a robbery. Eight years ago."

"Lost a lot of money?"

"Not very much."

34

"It was a pretty frightening experience for Henry, though, wasn't it?"

"Yes, it certainly was."

"Mrs. Devine, do you think that would have any effect at all on your ability to be impartial in the trial of a robbery case?"

"No, I don't think so."

"In other words," said MacInroth, "we would all agree that robbery is a pretty terrible thing, but we wouldn't want to convict anyone who isn't definitely proven guilty. Right?"

"That's right," agreed Mrs. Devine.

"All right. Thank you all," said MacInroth, and he walked back to his own seat and sat down.

The judge nodded to Bob Day.

Bob Day did not rise. He picked up his jury list and looked at it, then said, "Mr. Nicholas, can you hear me?"

Everyone looked at Day and then at Nicholas, and Nicholas looked at Jocelyn on one side of him and at Taylor on the other, then looked back to Day and did not respond.

"Mr. Nicholas, can you hear me?" Bob Day asked again, though not louder.

No response.

"Mr. Nicholas, you will be excused," said the judge loudly.

"What?" said Nicholas.

"You are excused. We don't think you can hear well enough."

Nicholas shrugged and rose from his seat. "Can I stay and listen?" he asked, pausing at the rail of the jury box.

"Certainly, if you want to," said the judge.

"I can't get a good seat now," said Nicholas sadly, looking back at the crowd in the courtroom. "I can't hear too well from 'way back there."

"Well, sit there in one of the chairs. Take the one Mrs. Brazington is giving up," said the judge, referring to the chair being vacated by juror number fifteen.

"Thank you, Judge," said Mr. Nicholas, and sat down. Bob Day was the first attorney to challenge him because of deafness. He had sat as a juror in two or three trials. Maybe some of the other attorneys knew he could not hear. I have heard lawyers say they like to have one juror, though not more than one, who cannot hear the trial. Probably it is a joke.

Bob Day rose and walked over to the jury box. "Mrs. Brazington," he said to the juror who had taken the number nine seat, "you have been listening to the questions asked of the members of the jury. Is there any reason why you could not serve?"

"No," she said. I don't know who Mrs. Brazington was. Never heard the name before. She looked like a housewife, and she was in her twenties. "Not related to any of the people we have been talking about?" Bob Day went on through the formula, and she said no again.

"All right," he said, and he looked up toward Martin. "Mr. Martin," he said, "I believe you said I once sent you a collection letter and you didn't owe the money. Is that right?"

"Yes," said Martin.

"I don't remember," Bob Day said thoughtfully. "Well, anyway, that wouldn't turn you against Ruth Gibson, my client, would it? In other words, it isn't her fault she has a stupid lawyer, is it?"

"No," said Martin.

"She didn't even choose me," Bob Day said. "The court appointed me to defend her because she doesn't have the money to pay for a lawyer. So if I sent you a mistaken letter, that isn't any fault of hers; right?" Some way he was bound to get it to the jury that the court had appointed him. It meant sympathy for his client, and it might shield him if his performance looked bad compared to those of his more experienced colleagues.

Martin, who by now did not want to be a party to Bob's demeaning himself, said, "Well, you probably thought I did owe it. I suppose the store told you I did, and you wouldn't have no way to know different."

"That's right. Thank you," said Bob. "Well, I would like to ask one more question. Does anyone have any trouble with this idea: that no one is guilty until proven so beyond any reasonable doubt? Is there anyone on the jury who doesn't agree that every accused is innocent until proven guilty beyond any reasonable doubt?" He had to get that in, too. I have never heard a juror respond to that question, and of course no one did this time.

Bob Day went back to his seat.

"Mr. Baumgardner," said the judge, "do you have any questions to ask of the newly seated jurors?" Baumgardner had the right to examine the jurors seated since he talked to the jury, but he shook his head. "Do you then wish to exercise a peremptory challenge?" the judge asked.

"We will excuse Mrs. Goodman," said Joe Baumgardner quietly and without rising. Of course I do not know why he challenged her—that is why it is a peremptory challenge; you don't have to say why you do it—but I suspect it was because of his experience with her during the other trials when she had been a juror. He had not had an acquittal this term, but his juries had been staying out a long time. Maybe one of the other jurors had told him that Mrs. Goodman was holding out for the defense. Maybe that was his motive, or maybe he just did not like the looks of her. We cannot know.

Mrs. Goodman got up and left the box, looking somewhat annoyed, and juror number sixteen took her place.

"Mrs. Krupa?" said Joe Baumgardner, consulting his list.

"That's right." Krupa, her husband, is a doctor—an osteopath, however. She is about thirty-five, mother of one child; a pretty, fat little woman.

"Is there any reason why you cannot render a fair verdict between these defendants and the State of Ohio?"

"No reason."

"You have heard all the questions and would not have any different answers to give?"

"No different answers."

Joe Baumgardner sat down, and MacInroth rose. "Mrs. Krupa, you are not acquainted with any of these people we have been talking about, are you?"

"Well, I know Mr. Garfield, of course," she said.

"But that would not influence your decision in any way, would it?"

"No."

MacInroth sat down, and Bob Day declined to question.

"Does the defense wish to exercise a challenge, Mr. MacInroth?" asked the judge.

"No, your honor," said MacInroth.

"Mr. Day?" asked the judge.

"No, your honor."

The challenge went back to the state then, and Joe Baumgardner spoke up and excused Martin. He probably thought Bob Day had established too much rapport in that exchange over the collection letter.

That brought up juror number seventeen, Mrs. Ross, who had said earlier that MacInroth and Fischer were handling her father-in-law's estate. Her husband was a farmer and sawmill operator. He was making money on the land.

"Mrs. Ross," said Joe Baumgardner, "I believe you said that Mr. MacInroth's office is doing some legal work with respect to the settling of the estate of your father-in-law. Is that right?"

"That's right."

"Are you then pretty well acquainted with Mr. MacInroth?"

"Yes, I would say so."

"Satisfied with the work he is doing for you?"

"Yes."

"You have a good attorney-client relationship."

"Well, it's my husband who is actually his client," she said.

Baumgardner turned to the judge, paused as if expecting Judge Kemp to speak, then said, "If the court please, I believe that this is sufficient grounds for excusing Mrs. Ross for cause."

"What cause?" asked the judge.

"That her husband employs Mr. MacInroth as his attorney."

"Well, that's not one of the statutory grounds," said Judge Kemp. "Mrs. Ross, do you think this fact will in any way influence your decision as a juror?"

"I don't think so," she said.

"You wouldn't vote to acquit just because Mr. MacInroth is the attorney for the defendant Louis? You understand that Mr. MacInroth can defend guilty people as well as innocent ones?"

"Yes, sir."

"I don't think there's cause," said the judge. Henry Kemp looked at me. I do my best to look blank when he does that. I don't want him to know whether I approve of his decisions or not. He is the judge now.

"Save an exception for the state," said Joe Baumgardner.

38

The judge shrugged. "It isn't necessary, but it will be noted," he said.

Joe Baumgardner sat down and nodded at MacInroth. MacInroth nodded to Bob Day, and Bob said, "No questions."

"Does the defense have a challenge, either of you?" the judge asked.

The two defense attorneys shook their heads.

"The state?" asked the judge.

"Mrs. Ross," said Joe Baumgardner. The state had eight peremptory challenges, and each of the defendants had four. The state had used three now, and the defense none.

That brought up juror number eighteen, and she moved up to take the seat vacated first by Martin and then by Mrs. Ross.

"Mrs. Koch?" said Joe Baumgardner to the lady who sat down.

"Yes, I am," she answered. Her husband was the Presbyterian minister. They transferred away shortly after the trial.

"Is there any reason, Mrs. Koch, why you could not serve as a juror in this case and render a fair and impartial verdict?"

"No reason at all," she said.

Joe Baumgardner seemed satisfied, and he passed the questioning to MacInroth. MacInroth had nothing to ask; neither did Day.

"Peremptory challenge for the defense?" asked Judge Kemp.

MacInroth shook his head, but Bob Day spoke up and excused Mrs. Koch. I know what he had in mind. Ministers and their wives do not make good jurors. They are apt to be narrow-minded. They have inflexible notions of right and wrong which interfere with their application of the law to the facts, and because they are ministers and ministers' wives they are apt to have too much influence on the other jurors.

Juror number nineteen moved up to take the place of Mrs. Koch, and he made the fourth person to sit in the number eleven seat. His name was Schwallie, a man from Pittsburgh sent here to manage a chain shoe store. He doesn't live here any more either. He was a nattily dressed young fellow of about twenty-five. Jocelyn, beside whom he had to sit, did not like the chain shoe store and did not like Schwallie.

Joe Baumgardner asked him the same questions and then

passed to MacInroth and Day who were perfunctory in their examination, so Schwallie was seated. He was obviously disgusted. This was the first time he had to sit since he had been called for jury duty.

Judge Kemp then asked Joe Baumgardner if he wanted to exercise the state's fourth peremptory challenge. Joe sat for a moment and looked at his jury list. Then he challenged Linnie Gardner, and therein he made a mistake, for Linnie was so crestfallen and disappointed as she left the courtroom to go back to her regular work that the other members of the jury could not help feeling sorry for her, and that made the prosecutor the villain. Little things like that can count.

Juror number twenty, Johnny Price, so christened—Johnny, not John—took Linnie's seat. He was just old enough to be a juror, twenty-two I think. He drove a truck for a living. He no sooner sat down than he turned around and looked at Miss Tubman's legs and made her give attention to her skirt. She tugged it down, while she and Taylor exchanged glances.

Joe Baumgardner began to question Price. "Johnny, you know any of these people?"

"I know Ruth there," he said, nodding in the direction of Ruth Gibson, the defendant.

"Know her pretty well, do you?"

"Well, I wouldn't say that. I've seen her around a lot."

"Do you know her well enough that the acquaintance would influence your decision as a juror?"

"Well, I don't know," he said hesitantly.

"Did you ever have a date with her, Johnny?" Baumgardner pressed.

"No, sir," said Johnny Price, quickly and affirmatively.

"Ever at a party where she was?"

"Yes."

"Talk to her?"

"Once in a while."

"You wouldn't want to see her go to the reformatory, would you?"

"Hell, no," he said positively, and then immediately he blushed and said toward the bench, "Excuse me, your honor."

"I think you can be excused," said the judge. He ran his hand through his graying black hair and looked to me and shook his head.

Juror twenty-one took the seat. David Ensign, son of Marshall County's thirty-year county auditor, a man of some forty-five years, bald with a fringe of black hair around the ear level. He worked for a building contractor as a bookkeeper and office manager. He fell to a peremptory challenge from MacInroth. MacInroth had absolutely humiliated the auditor, David's father, in a case a few years ago, made him out a fool on the witness stand, and MacInroth judged correctly that none of the Ensigns would ever forget it.

When juror twenty-two sat down we were in a pickle. She was the last juror we had. The jury commissioners had summoned thirty-six, enough for three juries. Fourteen had been excused by the court for various reasons—illness, hardship, profession, and so on—which left twenty-two. It was the first time in some years that we had ever used them all. The next time the jury commissioners would be instructed to draw fifty names from the wheel, but for the moment we were running out of jurors.

Juror number twenty-two was Mrs. Olivia Armstrong, a retired school teacher of some eighty years. She was a dear old soul. (Say I, who am ten years her senior!) She came forward, in her black dress, with her black straw hat covering her white hair, carrying her coat over her arm.

"Mrs. Armstrong," said Judge Kemp, "you are entitled to be excused if you want to be, since you are more than seventy years old."

"I am not too old to be a good juror," she said to him, and turning to Bob Day, added, "and I can hear every word you say."

"Do you know any of these people, Mrs. Armstrong?" asked Joe Baumgardner.

"Well, I guess I taught you all one time or another," she replied with a little smile.

"I guess you did," he said, returning her smile. "Do you know any reason why you could not render a fair and impartial decision in this case?"

"No, I don't."

Joe nodded to MacInroth. He asked no questions, nor did Day, although MacInroth turned to Day and made a comment.

"The state may exercise its fifth peremptory challenge," said Judge Kemp.

Joe Baumgardner shook his head.

"The defense?" asked the court.

Bob Day said, "We will excuse Mrs. Armstrong." This time the defense looked bad as the old lady scowled at Day and then gathered up her coat and stepped slowly out of the box. She looked up to the judge, who nodded, and she took the chair inside the rail from which she had come. She would stay and watch the trial. Bob Day excused her for the same reason that MacInroth had excused the minister's wife. Old people are apt to be settled in their moral concepts, are apt to be rigid. They do not approve of some of the conduct of the current generation. The defense had to see to it that the conduct of the current generation was judged by the standards of the current generation.

"Well," said the judge, "we'll have to send out for talesmen. See if you can get the sheriff in here, Quentin." Quentin bustled out to look for the sheriff, and the judge said to the attorneys, "We won't recess until we find out how much time this is going to take. Do you think you can pick a jury from six more people?"

The attorneys all nodded.

Then we waited, but not for long, because Quentin came back with the sheriff, George Ballentine, in less than three minutes. George came in in a hurry, with beads of sweat standing out on his flushed bald head. This is his second term as sheriff, but the job never ceases to mystify him. He probably thought the job would consist of riding around all day in a patrol car with a siren and red light.

"George, we're going to have to have talesmen," said the judge.

"Talesmen?" said the sheriff.

"Yes, more jurors. We've gone through the whole panel and don't have a jury picked yet. You'll have to go out and get us six more."

"Where am I gonna get 'em, Judge?" asked George.

"Around town, out on the street, not around the courthouse,

though. Just go out and summon them in here. People who would qualify to serve on a jury."

George nodded. "Six, you say?"

"Six. We'll recess for half an hour while you round them up."

"Okay," said George.

"The members of the jury so far picked are admonished," said the judge, "not to discuss what has taken place so far, either among themselves or with anyone else, during the recess. The court will be in recess for half an hour."

Henry Kemp came over to me. "Dammit," he said, "I was afraid this was going to happen. We've got to draw more damn jurors." Bill Mullen got up and made room, and Henry sat down beside me at the clerk's table. "Either that or I've got to quit excusing so damn many people."

I shrugged. "I'd have more names drawn, I think."

"Yes," he agreed.

The lawyers got up and went out. Roger Louis went back to talk to his father and that left Ruth Gibson sitting alone at the defense table. She looked around uneasily. Then Sally Ballentine, the sheriff's wife, came in and took her out. She probably wanted to go to the washroom. Everyone else did.

I went out to my office and looked over the morning mail, which had been delivered while I was in the courtroom. Joe Baumgardner came in and sat down.

"Good morning, Bill," he said to me. "What do you think?"

"I'm not paid to think any more," I said. "I just sit up there like an old bullfrog, and it looks like I'm paying attention, but I'm really thinking about flies."

"Where do you suppose George will get his talesmen?"

"Elks Club, Masonic Hall," I said. "There ought to be a suitable array of loafers around there."

"I was afraid he might go over and snag the customers around the table at Billy's and I'd have to challenge every one of them."

"Yes, you couldn't expect her regular customers to send her away. They probably like her pretty well."

"I should imagine," he said. "She's a bitch, Judge, that one is."

"Going to be an interesting trial, then?"

"Ahhh," he dismissed the prospect. "What can you do?"

"It will take a lot of convincing, Joe," I said.

"To make her out a bitch?"

"Yes."

"I don't think I'll even try." He lit a cigar. "I could, though. I could. But it's better that I concentrate on him."

"He doesn't look as pitiful as she does," I remarked.

"No. I can just about figure MacInroth. I've seen him in action enough. But I can't figure Bob yet. We're going to find out whether he's any good this time."

"Yes, we'll see," I said.

"Do you think the judge is disgusted with us for using up so many jurors?"

"Not especially. He's disgusted that more weren't drawn."

"Umm. Well, Judge, I think I had better go pee before I go back."

"You have plenty of time," I said.

I went back to the courtroom when there was still a little time to wait. George was back already with his talesmen, and they were standing around looking angry. It is an unsettling experience, I suppose, to be sitting in the lodge hall playing pinochle and have the sheriff come in and call you unexpectedly for jury duty. Roger Louis sat at one end of their table, while Ruth Gibson opposite him kept her eyes turned away from him. I had not seen them speak a word to each other. Most of the people had had their smoke and their visit to the toilets, and they were back in their seats. The word that we had sent out for talesmen was around town, and it had created additional interest in the trial, so there were a few new faces in the crowd. Two or three more attorneys were standing inside the rail, one talking to the judge and one talking to John MacInroth.

Bill Mullen sat down beside me again. "When the word got out that George was coming out looking for talesmen, it nearly cleared the streets," he said. "The merchants complain it has ruined business for the rest of the day."

When the half hour was over, Judge Kemp went back up to the bench, and things settled down again.

"Mr. Sheriff," said the judge, "have you summoned the talesmen?"

"Yes, your honor," said George. "I brought in these six gentlemen right here."

"Unless counsel have any objection, these six will be the talesmen," said the judge. The attorneys assented, and the judge motioned the first of them into the number one seat in the jury box.

Joe Baumgardner rose. "Will you state your name, please," he said to the man in the box.

"James E. Johnson," said the juror. I knew him, of course. He was a retired salesman for Procter and Gamble.

"You are a citizen and a voter in Marshall County?"

"Sure am."

"How old are you, sir?"

"Sixty-eight." Good. Not old enough to be excused, as he undoubtedly would have liked.

Baumgardner then went through with him all the questions he had asked the regular panel. So did MacInroth and Day. Johnson passed muster and was seated as juror number twenty-three in the number one seat. He was the fifth person to sit there.

It was the state's turn to exercise a peremptory challenge. Joe Baumgardner rose and said, "The jury is acceptable to the state."

MacInroth and Day then indicated that the jury was satisfactory to them. So we used only one of the talesmen.

The clerk of courts then came forward and swore the jury.

"You shall well and truly try, and true deliverance make between the State of Ohio and the defendants, Roger L. Louis and Ruth E. Gibson. So help you God."

"I do," each of the jurors muttered. I don't know why they say "I do." It does not fit the oath. But that is what they always say.

So we had a jury. Number one was James Johnson, sixty-eight years old, a retired salesman. Number two was Joe Paccinelli, family man who works for Gulf Oil. Number three was Mrs. James Krupa, wife of an osteopath. Number four was Janice O'Hara, dime-store clerk. Number five was William Cleveland, hill farmer. Number six was Mrs. Louis Teitelbaum, whose husband sells Chevrolets in an agency he and his brother own. Number seven was Linda Tubman, farm girl and waitress in a roadside beer joint. Number eight was Walter Taylor, meat cutter

45

in a supermarket. Number nine was Mrs. Clifton Brazington, housewife. Number ten was Edward Jocelyn, owner of Alexandria's largest store. Number eleven was Leon Schwallie, manager of a chain shoe store. Number twelve was Mrs. Henry Devine, wife of a cashier in a village branch of one of the local banks.

How do you judge a jury? Only by the results, I suppose, and this one, at this point in the trial, was as inscrutable as it is possible for mankind to be. You can never guess them. You can never figure which ones will be for you and which ones against. You never know what is in their minds.

So the jury faced the defendants, and the defendants faced their jury, all of them forming impressions of each other. I have never been a juror and I have never been a defendant on trial, so I do not pretend to know what jurors and defendants think about when they look at each other. There has been enough foolishness written about that anyway, so I will not add to it.

It was almost eleven-thirty. It had taken half the first day of the trial to pick a jury. Judge Kemp then decided to take the noon recess.

"The jurors are admonished again not to discuss the case with anyone or among themselves. The court will recess until one o'clock."

II

At noon, Judge Henry Kemp left for lunch with his wife, whose weak heart usually keeps her at home. The three attorneys, Baumgardner, MacInroth, and Day, went to their offices to check over their mail before lunch. Roger Louis and his family left to find a place in the center of town where they could eat without being embarrassed by surroundings too plush for them. Ruth Gibson was taken to the jail and would eat alone in her cell because there were no other women in jail. Bill Mullen went to the newspaper office to write his story for the afternoon paper. The jurors scattered. I strolled up the street to eat with my cronies at the big table at the Alexandria Bar and Grill.

John Kimball MacInroth is one of my cronies. We are not close friends but we do have lunch almost daily at the same table in the Alexandria back room. The big table seats a dozen men. The food is atrocious, but the company is pleasant, and a man never has to seek a luncheon companion and never has to eat alone. I had a Scotch and water before lunch, as I always do. By the time I was ready to order food MacInroth had come in and sat across the table from me. Six others were there besides MacInroth and me, but he wanted to talk to me, because I was the only one there who had been in the courtroom that morning.

He asked how I felt about the challenge of Mrs. Armstrong. "I think you made a mistake when you had Bob challenge Mrs. Armstrong," I said. "That old lady would have made a good juror, and you offended their sensibilities when you dismissed her."

"I didn't challenge her," MacInroth said. "I didn't tell Bob to do it, either. It was his own idea. He didn't ask me."

"Is that so?"

"That is so," MacInroth said. "That boy is independent. He's not taking instructions from me."

"No deference for his elders, eh?"

"None whatever."

"Well, what do you think of your jury?"

"They'll acquit us," he said flatly.

"Because the boy and girl are innocent?" I asked slyly.

"Well, they are," he said. "They are."

"All your clients are innocent, John," said one of the other men at the table.

"That's right," MacInroth said, biting deep into a sandwich.

I said, "The boy doesn't *look* innocent."

"Judge, I'm ashamed of you," MacInroth answered. "You ought to know how much appearances deceive. But I have to admit, he is a ratty-looking little bastard, ain't he?"

"The girl looks more innocent."

"Jesus, I wish I didn't have her in the case," he said, shaking his head.

"I imagine Joe Baumgardner's going to be able to show some embarrassing stuff about both of them."

"I'm afraid so," he conceded.

John MacInroth eats too much. He has ever since I have known him. He does not seem to gain weight, but he eats each meal as though it were his first, not his last. He enjoys it so, though, that people like to watch him at his meals. He gathers his food to him with enthusiasm, assaults it with vigor, and peppers his meals with comments on how good this and that is. Consequently, once he is served, there is very little conversation with him. Furthermore, once he has eaten he does not tarry at the table, but off he goes. So he was gone long before I was, and I saw him again only when we were back in the courtroom.

The afternoon session began as the morning had ended. The judge was still nervous, and he looked at me from time to time as if my presence helped him. The jurors were now resigned to the fact that they would be there until the trial ended, so they relaxed in their chairs. The two defendants tried to look calm and confident in their deliverance, when actually they were neither. They really understood only one fact about their trial: its importance to them. For the rest the unfamiliar surroundings and people and words bewildered them. I always pity simple people on trial. I do, no matter what crime they have really committed and are ultimately convicted of. To the lawyers and judges the trial is orderly and precise, even beautiful if you are a lawyer who appreciates the law that much; but the people on trial see no order or precision, and certainly no beauty in it. To them it must seem irrational, irregular, and grotesque. To us the trial means a careful examination of evidence and the application of the law to facts; to them it must mean an ordeal which they will or will not survive. Most lawyers and judges are blind to this difference. The law seems so fine to them, the culmination of centuries of Anglo-Saxon jurisprudence. Of course, they know what they are doing. It is too bad the subjects do not.

The opening statements were the next order of business, but before that the judge called upon all the witnesses to rise. Fifteen or more got to their feet. The clerk stepped to the rail and read the oath to them.

"You and each of you do solemnly swear that the testimony you are about to give in the cause in hearing will be the truth, the whole truth, and nothing but the truth as you shall answer to God. Say 'I do.'"

The witnesses nodded their heads and responded accordingly.

"Now," said the judge, "all the witnesses will leave the courtroom. You are not to watch or listen through the doors or leave the courthouse until you are excused."

Some of the witnesses complained as they filed out, as they always do. No one had told them differently, and they had assumed they would be allowed to sit and watch the trial. I am always amused by trials on television where the witnesses sit in the courtroom and watch, and a part of the drama is their reaction to the incidents of the trial. I have rarely seen a trial where the witnesses were allowed to stay in court before they took their turns on the stand. It is important that they be separated, as the phrase is. One lying witness must not be allowed to watch another lying witness undergo cross-examination; he could adjust his story to repair the weaknesses he saw in the testimony of his co-conspirator.

Judge Kemp nodded to Joe Baumgardner, and Joe rose to make his opening statement. He stood at his table at first, with a sheaf of papers in his hand, and he put his other hand in his coat pocket as he began to speak.

"Ladies and gentlemen of the jury, as most of you know, we now come to that part of the trial known as the opening statements. The purpose of the opening statements is to tell you in advance what the case you are going to try is all about, so you will know what the witnesses are talking about when they take the stand and tell their stories. First the prosecution and then the defense will tell you what they expect to prove in this case. That is the purpose of the opening statements.

"These two defendants, Roger Louis and Ruth Gibson, are on trial here because they are charged with the crime of armed robbery. They were indicted by the grand jury. I will read you the indictments."

He laid aside all his papers except two large white sheets, and he began to read:

"The State of Ohio, Marshall County. Of the Term of our Court of Common Pleas for September in the Year of our Lord one thousand nine hundred and sixty-one.

"The jurors of the Grand Jury of the State of Ohio, within and for the body of the County aforesaid, on their oaths, in the name and by the authority of the State of Ohio, do find and present that Roger Larimer Louis, on the twentieth day of May, 1961, at the County of Marshall aforesaid, did, while armed with a pistol, by force and violence and by putting in fear, rob Paul A. Russell of certain jewelry, being watches and rings, of the value of three thousand one hundred dollars, and money in the amount of two hundred one dollars and eighty-four cents, being the property of DeWitt Jewelry Company, Incorporated, an Ohio corporation, contrary to the form of the statute in such case made and provided, and against the peace and dignity of the State of Ohio. Signed Joseph T. Baumgardner, Prosecuting Attorney. Indorsed, A True Bill, and signed Victor A. Carnahan, Foreman of the Grand Jury."

Joe Baumgardner laid the first indictment aside and read the second:

"The State of Ohio, Marshall County. Of the Term of our Court of Common Pleas for September in the Year of our Lord one thousand nine hundred and sixty-one.

"The jurors of the Grand Jury of the State of Ohio, within and for the body of the County aforesaid, on their oaths, in the name and by the authority of the State of Ohio, do find and present that Ruth Elaine Gibson, on the twentieth day of May, 1961, at the County of Marshall aforesaid, did, while armed with a pistol, by force and violence and by putting in fear, rob Paul A. Russell of certain jewelry, being watches and rings, of the value of three thousand one hundred dollars, and money in the amount of two hundred one dollars and eighty-four cents, being the property of DeWitt Jewelry Company, Incorporated, an Ohio Corporation, contrary to the form of the statute in such case made and provided, and against the peace and dignity of the State of Ohio. Signed Joseph T. Baumgardner, Prosecuting Attorney. Indorsed, A True Bill, and signed Victor A. Carnahan, Foreman of the Grand Jury."

Having read the indictments somewhat rapidly, Joe Baumgardner paused for breath as he put down the last paper. He seemed to be looking for a place to begin; after a moment he found it.

"Now, ladies and gentlemen," he said, "these two indictments charge the crime of armed robbery. In other words, they charge that Roger Louis and Ruth Gibson held up this young man, Paul Russell, at the point of a gun and stole money and jewelry from him at the place where he works, the DeWitt Jewelry Company. To establish that crime the state has to prove two things to you.

It has to prove first that something was stolen, something of value. And second, it has to prove that that theft took place by the use of a dangerous weapon which caused Paul Russell to hand over the things that were stolen because he was in fear for his life and safety.

"The state expects to prove to you, beyond any doubt reasonable or otherwise, that at nine o'clock in the morning of the twentieth day of May, 1961, Roger Louis walked into the DeWitt store, as he had been long planning to do, and that he pointed a gun at Paul Russell—Doc Russell—the clerk in the store, and told him to fill up a paper bag, which he then handed him, with money and jewelry. The state will prove that Paul Russell, being afraid that he would be shot, did what Roger Louis told him to do and filled up the bag with money from the cash register and watches and rings from the showcase. The state will prove that Roger Louis then told Paul Russell to lie down on the floor behind the counter and stay there until he, Louis, was gone, or he would kill him. Roger Louis then left the store with his paper sack full of loot and returned to his automobile, where his girl friend, Ruth Gibson, was waiting for him. They then drove away. But not until Paul Russell had run to the window of the store and looked out and had seen Ruth Gibson in the car."

The prosecuting attorney moved from his table toward the jury box.

"The state will prove that Ruth Gibson planned this crime for her boy friend, her lover, to carry out. We will prove that Ruth Gibson, as the phrase is, 'cased the joint' and found the best time to commit the robbery. We will prove that Ruth Gibson struck up a friendship with Paul Russell for the purpose of extracting information from him about the store and how to rob it. We will prove, ladies and gentlemen," said the prosecutor on a rising voice, "that Ruth Gibson tried to recruit Paul Russell to assist her in carrying out this crime and that she taunted him for being a coward when he refused.

"The state will prove, ladies and gentlemen, that this pair fled from the scene of their crime, knowing they had been recognized and identified, and that therefore they hid out, hoping to evade capture, and that they resisted arrest because they knew they had been found out in the act.

"In short, ladies and gentlemen of the jury, the State of Ohio has accused this pair of the crime of armed robbery, and the State of Ohio will prove beyond any doubt whatever that they are guilty as charged."

Baumgardner sat down. MacInroth and Day conferred for a moment in whispers, and then Bob Day rose to make the opening statement for the defense. It was the first time any of us had seen him perform. He had tried a few minor suits and some traffic violations, but now he was trying his first important case. His wife and father and mother were in the rear of the courtroom, and as he walked toward the jury box I saw him glance back toward his family. His wife touched her mouth and sat up straighter.

"Ladies and gentlemen," Bob Day began in an easy tone, betraying not the slightest sign of nervousness, "the most interesting thing about opening statements prosecutors make is that they are always wild and bold. They always promise to prove a lot of fearful things. They make those promises because they want to convince you right now, at the beginning, before any evidence is heard, that the people they accuse are guilty of the things they are accused of. Unfortunately for prosecutors, trials don't end right here; they have to back up their statements with evidence. The jury will decide if the evidence proves the things the prosecutor promises to prove.

"I say to you—the defense says to you—that the prosecution will not prove all these things. Far from it. Oh, you are going to hear witnesses testify to most of these things, but the defense will show you that that testimony does not prove what they say it proves.

"Now, ladies and gentlemen, the defense has filed, because the law says it must file, a paper with the court which is called a notice of alibi. In that paper the defense has notified the prosecution that we intend to prove to you that at the time when the alleged robbery was supposed to be taking place Roger Louis was not at DeWitt's store." Bob Day paused for effect. "Roger Louis was not even in Alexandria. No, Roger Louis was twenty miles away with a group of his friends, asleep in a sleeping bag along the banks of Greenwater Creek, where he and his friends had been fishing all night. The burden of proof is on the prosecution, ladies and gentlemen. They must prove the guilt of Roger Louis, as you know and as the court will instruct you later. The defense does not have to prove the innocence of these two young people. But we will prove it. We will prove it because we will prove that when the supposed robbery took place Roger Louis was not there nor anywhere near, and so he could not have held up Doc Russell at the point of a gun. This we will prove, to your entire satisfaction, and beyond any doubt whatever.

"This is the defense of Roger Louis. Simply, this is his defense. But we will also show that there is strong reason to suspect that Doc Russell knowingly and falsely accuses him for reasons of his own. We will show that there is reason to suspect that no robbery took place at all. But, if there was a robbery, it will make no difference to this trial, because we have incontrovertible evidence which proves beyond any question that Roger Louis did not commit it."

Bob Day stepped back to the prosecutor's table and leaned against it, speaking in a voice less strident than he had used during the last few sentences.

"I need hardly point out, then, ladies and gentlemen, what Ruth Gibson's defense is. You will remember from the statement of the prosecuting attorney that she is not accused of holding up anyone with a gun. She is accused of plotting a robbery which Roger Louis is supposed to have carried out, of that and of sitting in the car while he went in and used a gun to commit the crime. In other words, to use the technical term, she is accused of being an accessory, an aider and abettor, of the crime which Roger Louis is accused of having committed. Now, ladies and gentlemen, obviously—" he said, and the reporter looked up as Bob's voice dropped. Moving close to the jury box, Bob continued— "obviously, if Roger Louis did not commit the crime, then Ruth Gibson could not have helped him to do it. Right? That is her defense. Her defense is tied to his. She could not help him commit a crime unless he did commit one, and he did not commit one, as we will prove."

He walked away from the jury box and clear across the front of the courtroom until he stood before his chair at the defense table. Resting his hands on the table he went on. "I want to ask

54

you, ladies and gentlemen, to keep your attention focused throughout this trial on the one basic issue. Did Roger Louis commit armed robbery? That is all we are here to decide. Nothing else. I suspect there will be an attempt to distract your attention from that one issue. We will probably have to listen to a lot of talk about a lot of other things. But there is only one issue at trial here, and that is: Did Roger Louis commit armed robbery? Let's not forget it.

"Finally, ladies and gentlemen, we ask you to remember one more thing: Until they are proved guilty beyond any reasonable doubt, these two young people are innocent, even as you and I are innocent until the state proves us guilty of some crime. Let us never lose sight of that principle."

Bob sat down. There was some stirring in the courtroom. His speech had impressed the crowd.

It *was* a good speech, even if a little argumentive for an opening statement. All attorneys, even young ones, fall into that habit, and judges let them. I was interested to notice that he did not say he would try to prove that even if Roger Louis did commit the crime she did not help him. He had tied her defense to the boy's completely. Thus the defense conceded a point. It might be that MacInroth had simply convinced him that the two of them had to stand or fall together. Or he might have had something else in mind. But it was an interesting point, and I wondered if anyone on the jury had caught it.

I had noticed the two defendants during the opening statements. Louis had kept his eyes down toward the table, but Ruth Gibson had watched both lawyers. She had watched Bob Day very closely, and when he sat down she smiled briefly and whispered to him.

"The state may call its first witness," said Judge Kemp.

Joe Baumgardner turned to the bailiff and said, "Call Paul Russell."

Quentin hurried out the side door to bring in the witness, and while he was out the spectators had their moment to cough and scratch and shuffle. Then he came in with Paul Russell. The witness walked confidently across the room without having to be told where to go, and sat down in the witness box.

"You've been sworn?" asked the judge.

"Yes, sir," replied Russell, nodding. He was a tall young man of about twenty-five, thin and bony, with sharp features; his eyes were light blue, and he had abundant blond hair brushed back. He was dressed in a dark blue suit with a white shirt and a blue bow tie with little white dots.

"State your full name, please," said Joe Baumgardner.

"Paul T. Russell."

"Where do you live?"

"Six fifty-six Meigs Street, Alexandria."

"Where do you work?"

"I work at DeWitt's, the jewelry store."

"How long have you worked there?"

"For five years, sir. Before that I worked there on a part-time basis when I was in high school."

Joe Baumgardner remained seated at his table while he asked these questions. The witness sat forward on his chair and held his hands clasped on the front of the witness box. His voice was distorted. He was too plainly trying to speak precisely and with a tone and enunciation that could be heard by all—trying to sound as he thought a witness should sound instead of the way he would ordinarily.

"You've been in the service?"

"Yes, sir. In the army two years."

"Are you married?"

"No, sir."

"Now, Paul. . . . Incidentally, you are usually called Doc, aren't you?"

"Yes, sir."

"For any particular reason?"

"Not that I know of, sir. They always called me that, since I was a kid."

"All right then. You were in DeWitt's on the morning of May twenty, were you not?"

"Yes, sir. That was a Saturday, and the store would be open."

"Yes. At what time did you arrive that morning?"

"About eight-thirty."

"Would that be your usual time to arrive in the store?"

56

"Yes, sir."

"What time does the store open?"

"Nine o'clock, sir."

"Why do you go in at eight-thirty?"

The witness sat back in his chair a bit, and his voice eased. Now he was talking about something familiar. "Well, sir, I open the store for Mr. Garfield. There is about half an hour's work to do before we open the doors. I don't have any sweeping to do— that's done for us at night. But I usually give the walk a quick once-over. It has butts on it and so forth. Then I get the lights on, unlock the cash register, and open the safe and put the trays of jewelry in the showcases."

"You have the combination to the safe yourself?"

"Yes, sir. Only Mr. Garfield has the key to a locked compartment inside the safe, but I can open the main safe."

"You put all the jewelry in the safe at night?"

"Not everything, sir. We put away the better things. We put away the diamonds, of course, and the better pieces of jewelry, and the better watches. They're kept in trays in the showcases, and we just pick up the trays and slide them into the safe. They fit into slots in the safe."

"And you do that before the store opens?"

"Yes, sir. Mr. Garfield likes to have everything ready for business when we open the doors. The showcases would look drab if people came in and saw them before we put in the merchandise."

"How much cash would be in the cash register at that time of day?"

"When we close in the afternoon, Mr. Garfield takes out all the cash except about two hundred dollars and takes it up the street to the night depository at the bank. We keep the two hundred or so on hand for the next day's change. It would all be in small bills and silver."

"You put that in the safe?"

"No, sir, that is left in the cash register."

"Who else is in the store besides you at that time of day? I mean ordinarily."

"Ordinarily I would be alone in the store at that time of day," replied the witness. He was still phrasing carefully.

"When does Mr. Garfield ordinarily come in?"

"About nine-thirty or a quarter to ten. He almost always has breakfast with his friends before he comes in, and then when he comes in I go out to eat."

"You are not the only clerk?"

"No, sir. There are two others who work in the store—Sally Garfield, Mr. Garfield's daughter, and a woman named Irene Grestlinger."

"When do they come in?"

"On weekdays they come in at nine o'clock, but since we are open Saturday evenings, they don't come in until noon on Saturdays. I leave at five on Saturdays, the same as I do other days, and they stay and run the store Saturday evenings."

"So on Saturday would be the only time when you would be alone in the store at nine o'clock?"

"I object to his leading the witness," said Bob Day quietly.

"Put it this way then," said Joe Baumgardner, without waiting for the ruling of the court. "Would you ordinarily be alone in the store at nine o'clock on any other day of the week except Saturday?"

"No."

"Thank you. Do you ordinarily have customers in by nine o'clock?"

"Not usually, sir. Occasionally we will have. But our business usually picks up about ten and is brisk for the rest of the day."

"Now," said Joe Baumgardner, rising to move over by the jury box, "referring again to May 20, 1961, will you describe what happened that morning."

"Yes, sir," said the witness, gathering in his breath and shifting in his chair. "I came downtown at the usual time and was in the store by eight-thirty. The walk was exceptionally dirty that morning, so I brought out the hose and hosed it off. Then I went back inside and put the hose away and washed my hands, and I opened the safe and took out the trays of jewelry and put them in the cases. I unlocked the cash register and counted the money and made a note of it for Mr. Garfield. Then I turned on the store lights and looked around for a final check of things before

58

I opened. I still had a few minutes, so I went back to the work room and checked the watches that were in for repair against the chronometer to see if they were keeping good time. Mr. Garfield does most of the watch repairing, but I do some of the adjusting. Then I came out, and it was nine o'clock, so I went to the door and raised the blind and unlocked the door. There was a man there waiting, and so I let him in."

"Now let me interrupt you," said Joe Baumgardner. "Is that man in the courtroom?"

"Yes, he is."

"Can you point him out?"

"That's him, sitting over there," said Doc Russell, pointing to Roger Louis.

Roger Louis shook his head vigorously. There was a stir in the courtroom.

"Let the record show," said Joe Baumgardner, "that the witness has identified the defendant Roger Louis. How was he dressed, Mr. Russell?"

"He was wearing dark blue trousers, a white shirt, and a blue jacket."

"A sport-coat type of jacket?"

"No, a winter jacket with a zipper up the front."

"Was he wearing a hat?"

"No, sir."

"Go ahead."

"Well, sir, I asked him what I could do for him, and he didn't say anything. I went behind the counter, and he walked back into the store, with me following him, only I was behind the counter. When we were well back into the store, he took this pistol out of his jacket pocket and pointed it at me."

"What did he say?"

"Well, he gave me a brown paper sack he had in his left hand and he told me to open the cash register and put the money in it."

"What did you do?"

"I did what he told me. When I had put all the cash we had in the sack, he told me to fill the sack up with other stuff. I tried

59

to pick less expensive things, but he pointed to the trays I had taken out of the safe. I poured several trays of rings and watches into the sack, and then suddenly he told me to give him the sack. I handed it back to him, and he told me to lie down on the floor behind the counter, and he said if I got up he would shoot me. He told me to stay there. I heard him go out the door. I've heard that door close for so many years, that I know just when it closed. As soon as I heard it close I ran to the front of the store and looked out. I could see him getting in a car."

"Let me ask you what kind of a car."

"A light green Chevrolet. An old one, a forty-nine or fifty or somewhere along in there."

"Where was it parked?"

"Just up the street one door, in front of Ted's Men's Shop."

"Did you see the license number?"

"No, sir. I wasn't looking at that. I was looking at him, and I was looking at the girl that was with him."

"Be a little more specific please. You were looking at *who?*"

"Well, I was looking at Roger Louis getting in the car, and then I saw Ruth Gibson sitting in the car."

"Can you identify Ruth Gibson in the courtroom?"

"Yes, sir, that's her sitting right over there."

"Let the record show the witness has identified the defendant Ruth Gibson."

Ruth Gibson did not shake her head. She just sat looking steadily at Doc Russell, and I thought I noticed that he avoided looking at her.

"Did she see you?"

"Yes, sir, I thought she did," said the witness. "She was looking right at me. She said something to Louis, and he turned around and looked at me too. Well, I was afraid he would come back and shoot me because I had seen her and she knew I knew her, so I ran back through the store and out the back door into the alley."

"Where did you go?"

"I ran in the back door of Ted's Men's Shop. I told them what had happened, and they looked out the front, and the car was gone. Then they called the police."

"All right, Mr. Russell, now I want to ask you how much cash you had in the register when you counted it that morning before the robbery."

"Two hundred and one dollars and eighty-four cents. I had written it down for Mr. Garfield."

"And you put it all in the paper bag?"

"Yes, sir, all of it."

"Now, Mr. Russell, you have heard some talk since then about the value of the jewelry that was stolen, but I want you to tell us what you yourself think it was worth, based on your experience in the jewelry business."

"Well, we checked over the inventory, and I know what items were missing and what we paid for them wholesale."

"All right, what was the value of what was missing?"

"It was a little over three thousand dollars wholesale. That would be considerably more in retail value."

"Yes. All right, now tell us, did you ever see Roger Louis before that morning?"

"I may have. Not that I know of."

"You were not acquainted with him?"

"No, sir."

"Didn't know his name?"

"No, sir."

"How about Ruth Gibson, did you know her?"

"Yes, sir."

"How well did you know her?"

"Pretty well. I had several dates with her."

"When was that?"

"Last winter."

"Several months before the robbery?"

"I think I had my last date with her in March or the first of April."

"Several weeks before the robbery, then?"

"Yes, sir."

"How did you become acquainted with her?"

"Well, she worked as a waitress up the street there at Billy's."

"By Billy's you mean Reitlinger's Restaurant?"

"Yes, sir."

"And you met her there?"

"Yes, sir. I used to eat there some, and I went in for a drink sometimes in the evening. I got to know her, so I asked her to go out with me."

"And she accepted?"

"Yes, sir."

"Readily?"

"Yes, sir."

"Was she, do you know, in the habit of making dates with her customers?"

"Objection!" said Bob Day.

"If the court please," said the prosecutor in a patient tone, but without giving Day the time to state the reason for his objection, "I am not trying to show that Ruth Gibson was a tramp waitress who would allow men to pick her up. To the contrary, I expect to show that she would not accept dates with her customers, though they tried to date her often. I want to show that she departed from her habit to accept dates with this young man for the purpose of setting up this robbery."

"We will let it in," said Judge Kemp uneasily.

"Do you remember the question?" asked the prosecutor in a tone of exaggerated fatigue.

"Yes, sir. No, I had heard her often refuse dates to other men around the place. That's why I was surprised when she agreed to go out with me."

"So you had dates with her, then," said Baumgardner. "How many, would you say?"

"Oh, a dozen at least."

"Or more?"

"Yes, sir. Or more."

"Did you like her?" Russell didn't answer, so he repeated the question. "Did you like her?"

The witness turned his head toward Ruth Gibson, who was still looking at him steadily, and he dropped his eyes as he said, "Yes, I did."

"Were you in love with her?"

"No, sir. I wouldn't say that," he said, now regaining his composure and gathering in his breath.

"Did she ever tell you that she loved you?"

"No, sir."

"Were you intimate with her?"

"I beg your pardon, sir?"

"Well, did you kiss her?"

"Yes, sir."

"Did she allow you to do more than that?"

"Yes, sir."

"Well, did you have sexual intercourse with her?"

"No, sir," said the witness firmly.

"But you would say that you were physically intimate?"

"Yes, sir."

"Did she allow you intimacies on your first date with her?"

"Objection," said Bob Day. "This has gone far enough. It has no relevance whatever. It is prejudicial, or meant to be."

"If your honor please," said the prosecutor, "all this is intended to bring out the method used by the defendant to extract information from this young man about his place of employment."

"That's ridiculous," said Day.

"Well, Mr. Baumgardner, I don't like it much," said the judge. "I'll let you go on a question or two more, but you better show how it is relevant pretty quick. It doesn't require the details."

"Thank you, your Honor," said Joe Baumgardner. He went over to his table and sat down. He looked up at the witness and considered his question for a moment, and then he asked, "Well, Mr. Russell, do you think that Ruth Gibson tried from the first to win your affection and confidence?"

"Objection," said Bob Day.

"We'll hear the answer," said the judge.

"Yes, sir. I thought she did. Or at least I think so now."

"And did she do so by allowing you a high degree of physical intimacy from the time of your first date with her?"

"Objection."

"Overruled."

"Yes, sir. I think she let me take liberties that most girls would not have permitted on our first date."

"Now I object," said Bob Day, rising. "It is irrelevant and prejudicial; it is an opinion. I ask that it be stricken and the jury be instructed to disregard it."

"The jury is instructed," said Judge Kemp slowly and carefully, "that evidence of the defendant Ruth Gibson's moral conduct with this witness is allowed only to let Mr. Baumgardner try to show she tried to seduce information from the witness. *If* he can show it. Her sexual habits are not a matter with which we are concerned, and you are instructed not to consider this testimony as character evidence."

He paused and thought about what he had said. He knew and I knew and the lawyers knew that his instruction would have absolutely no effect, but he could say nothing else. If Baumgardner could show that the girl used her body to tease Doc Russell into telling her when he would be alone in the store with a supply of cash and jewelry, that could be important evidence, and the judge could not exclude it. On the other hand, a discussion of the girl's sex life could prejudice the jury irretrievably.

"Mr. Baumgardner," the judge said then, "have you made your point now? Can we get out of this touchy area?"

"If the court please, I will get out of it as quickly as I can."

"Do so, Mr. Baumgardner."

"Now, sir," said the prosecutor to the witness, "you have told us that the girl allowed you a high degree of physical intimacy and you said you liked her and she seemed to like you. What then went wrong with the relationship?"

"Would he care," interrupted Bob Day, "to establish first that something did go wrong with the relationship?"

"Very well, Mr. Day," said the prosecutor. "We shall find out. Mr. Russell, how long did you continue to go out with Miss Gibson?"

"For about two months."

"Why did you quit going out with her?"

"Because we got into an argument about robbing the store."

"All right. Describe that."

"Well, when we went out we talked a lot about our work. She talked about the restaurant, and I talked about the store. I realize now that she asked me a lot of questions about the store."

"Like what?"

"Well, all kinds of questions. She came in sometimes too and

64

looked around. I guess she got to know pretty well how the store was run. Then one night she said to me, 'We could take a little money out of the store, Doc, and old man Garfield would never know the difference.'"

"What did you say to that?"

"Nothing much. I thought she was joking."

"Did she bring it up again?"

"Yes, she did. The next time we were out she talked about how poor we are and how we never get ahead much and never can have the things other people have. Then she said we could fake a robbery of the store and take out a lot of money, and nobody would ever know the difference. She said Mr. Garfield trusted me and let me open the store alone, and she could come to the back door, and I could give her a sack full of money and jewelry, and she could go back to the restaurant, and I could say I was robbed."

"What did you say?"

"I told her not to talk like that. I still thought she was kidding."

"Where were you when she said all this?"

"In my car."

"Were you in your car every time she said it?"

"Yes, sir."

"How many times did she make this proposition?"

"Well, lots of times. She kept it up, and we began to fight about it."

"Fight?"

"Yes, I would try to make her stop talking about it. I didn't believe she really meant it. I thought it was a joke she was teasing me with."

"Did she ever suggest that someone else would come in and stage the robbery?"

"Yes, she said maybe we ought to have someone come in like he was robbing me."

"Did she suggest anyone for the purpose?"

"No."

"Did she withdraw from you when you would not talk about the idea?"

65

"Yes, she wouldn't let me kiss her. She got cold."

"Did you finally convince her you would not participate in such a plot?"

"I guess I did."

"Then what happened?"

"One night she got real mad about it. She said I didn't have the guts to do it, wasn't man enough, and things like that. After that she wouldn't go out with me."

"You tried to date her after that?"

"Well, I tried to talk to her at Billy's. She said she didn't want to talk to me any more."

"And when was that, with reference to the time of the robbery?"

"A month or six weeks before."

"Did she ever talk to you again after that?"

"No, I quit going to Billy's. I saw her on the street after that, and I may have seen her here and there in places where I might go for a drink, but she never talked to me. I didn't go near her after that."

"Did you see her after she was arrested?"

"Yes, sir. I saw her in the jail."

"Describe that occasion."

"Well, I identified Louis in the sheriff's office, and then they asked me to identify her, so they took me back to the jail. She was in there, and I identified her."

"Did she say anything to you?"

"Yes, she said it was the sort of thing she would have expected me to do."

Joe Baumgardner looked to his papers. After examining them for a moment, he turned to the defense table and said, "You may cross-examine."

"The court will recess for fifteen minutes," said the judge. "The jurors are again admonished not to discuss the case or to form any opinions about it until all the evidence is heard."

III

When we returned to the courtroom, MacInroth began to cross-examine Paul Russell. He remained seated at his table, with his notes from Baumgardner's direct examination before him.

"Doc, has any of the jewelry taken in the robbery you described been recovered, to your knowledge?"

"No, sir. Not to my knowledge."

"Was any of it the sort of thing which could be identified?"

"Some of it could be."

"If a piece of jewelry or a watch were shown to you, could you identify it? By that I mean could you tell whether it was one of the pieces taken in the robbery?"

"Probably I could. Some of the watches and diamonds could be identified individually. Other things could just be identified by type."

"But none of the stuff has shown up?"

"No."

"In other words, it was not found on or about the two defendants when they were arrested or in their homes when they were searched?"

"Well, they could have disposed of it."

"I appreciate your explaining that, but I will appreciate more your confining your answers to the questions asked," MacInroth said gently.

"Yes, sir," the witness replied curtly.

"You haven't seen any of it, then? Nothing has been found?"

"That's right."

"That's too bad, isn't it?"

"Yes, it is."

"Tell me, Doc, do you still open the safe over at the store?"

The witness kept silent for a moment, looking hard at the attorney, and then he said, "No, I don't."

"Why don't you?"

Again the witness hesitated, and then he said, "The combination has been changed."

"When was it changed?" asked MacInroth quickly, stepping up the pace of his questioning.

"A few days after the robbery."

"And Mr. Garfield has not told you the new combination?"

"No."

"Why is that, do you suppose?"

"I don't know."

"You don't know?"

"That's what I said."

MacInroth glanced quickly at Bob Day. He had irritated the witness, and he was pleased by it. An experienced trial lawyer knows that an irritated witness promises fruitful cross-examination. I sensed he felt the cross-examination would be successful.

"How long had you been opening the safe, Doc?"

"I don't know exactly."

"Well, was it two weeks?"

"No, longer than that."

"Two years?"

"Yes, two years or more. Maybe three years. I don't remember when he first told me the combination."

"All that time, and then two days after the robbery he changes the combination and won't let you open it anymore, and you don't know why?"

"I didn't say two days. I said a few days."

"Okay, he lets you open it for two or three years, but a few days after the robbery he changes the combination and won't let you open it anymore, but you don't know why?"

"No, I don't know why."

"He never told you why?"

"Your honor, the witness has said he doesn't know why," said Baumgardner.

"Proceed, Mr. MacInroth, proceed," said the judge quickly, shaking his flat hand toward the attorney.

"All right. Doc, have you heard rumors around town to the effect that there was no robbery? Have you heard that it is being said that you yourself took the jewelry and money and invented the story of the robbery to cover yourself?"

"No, I haven't," the witness said positively, and here he made a mistake, for nearly every member of the jury had heard the gossip about this case. They knew Paul Russell could not have avoided hearing it too. Two or three of the jurors stirred in their seats and moved into more alert postures.

"Of course if you heard such a rumor you would deny it?"

"I haven't heard anything like that," said the witness blandly.

"Mr. Garfield never said to you that he has heard a rumor like that?" asked MacInroth in his best incredulous voice.

"No."

"But he doesn't seem to trust you as much as he did, does he?"

"I object to that," said Baumgardner.

"I'll withdraw the question," said MacInroth. "But he doesn't let you open the safe anymore, does he?"

"If the court please," said Baumgardner, rising to his feet, "we have been over that about five times. If Mr. MacInroth wants to argue the case now, the state would be willing to rest on what it has in evidence and proceed to final argument."

"Yes, it does seem as if we've heard enough of that one question," said the judge.

"All right. I'm sorry. The fact *is* established now. So let me ask you this, Doc. If someone is convicted of robbing you, that would get you off the hook, wouldn't it?"

"Objection."

"I'll let the witness answer, and then we'll go on to something else," said Judge Kemp.

"Do you remember the question?" asked MacInroth.

"Yes."

"Well, then, you can answer."

"I don't know what you mean."

"Well, do you want the question explained?"

"No, Mr. MacInroth," the judge interrupted. "He says he doesn't know what you mean to imply, and that is an answer to your question. Go on to something else."

"Yes, your Honor. I will," MacInroth agreed. He could very well do that. He had made his point. He had given the witness a motive for lying. Now everything Paul Russell said would be suspect. Only slightly suspect, I thought, but suspect nevertheless.

"Did it rain the morning of the robbery?" MacInroth asked.

The witness thought for a moment and then said, "I don't remember."

"Well, you remember a lot of detail about things that morning—what you did in the store down to the last detail—but you say you can't remember whether it rained?"

"No, I don't remember."

"Well, you say you sprayed the walk with the hose. Would you have done that if it had rained?"

"I might. Just as much trash accumulates on a sidewalk on a rainy day as on any other."

MacInroth was fishing, and this time he had caught nothing. He turned to something else. "Doc, you have testified about what you called physical intimacies you say Ruth Gibson let you have with her. Do I recall your saying that she never did let you have sexual intercourse with her?"

"No, she never did," said the witness positively.

"Good," returned MacInroth in a tone which caused a burst of laughter in the courtroom. "But you did have physical intimacies. What do you mean by that?"

"If the court please," said Joe Baumgardner, "the defense objected when I asked such a question."

"And the court allowed it," interrupted MacInroth, "and the prosecution pursued it."

"We will have to allow it," ruled the judge. "I hope that a certain amount of propriety can be preserved."

"The question, Doc, was what do you mean by physical intimacies?"

"Well—" said the witness hesitantly. He was just as uncomfortable as MacInroth meant him to be. "We necked."

"By that do you mean that you kissed her?"

"Yes."

"And hugged her?"

"Yes."

"And touched her breasts?"

"Well, I . . . don't remember that specifically."

"You testified," said MacInroth in a larger voice, rising from the table and walking over to stand by the jury box, "that she allowed you a surprising or improper amount of physical intimacy. Do you mean to say that did not include touching her breasts?"

Russell considered for a moment and then said, "I don't entirely understand the question."

"Well, let's get back to the original point. I asked what you meant by physical intimacy. Did it include touching her breasts?"

"I suppose sometimes it did," the witness returned quickly.

"And her legs? You touched her legs?"

"Yes, sometimes."

"Did you undress her?"

Russell looked up to the judge as if in an appeal to stop the questions. He looked to the prosecutor for an objection. Then he said, "No," in a strong voice. I am sure not one member of the jury believed him.

"Very well," said MacInroth, "and we will draw the veil of propriety at that point. Unless you want to describe some further intimacy you had with her? Do you?"

"No."

"All right. Will you agree then that what you mean by physical intimacy you had with Ruth Gibson is that you kissed her and hugged her and touched her breasts and legs but did not take her clothes off? Do you agree?"

"Yes," said the witness, and no one in the courtroom could have failed to sense that he was glad to conclude it that way.

"All right," said MacInroth. "Now, Doc, you drive a little red Ford, don't you?"

"Yes, sir."

"This intimacy with Ruth Gibson took place in that car, didn't it?"

"Yes."

"How many other girls have you taken out and parked with during the last, oh let us say, six months?"

Russell paused again as though expecting help. "I don't know, maybe a couple others," he said finally.

"During the past year?"

"Maybe three."

"Then during the past several years, perhaps a dozen or more, right? If I were to issue a flock of subpoenas to girls I myself have seen you with, I could bring into this courtroom perhaps a dozen girls around town that have been out and parked along the roads in your car with you, couldn't I?"

"I suppose so."

"You do that occasionally, Doc, when you can, don't you? Go out and park, I mean?"

"Yes, sir, occasionally."

"In the nighttime?"

"Usually."

"After dark?"

"Usually."

"What do you do on these occasions?"

"Nothing much," said Russell. He was a little angry.

"Well, do you have what you have called physical intimacies with those girls?"

"Well, I wouldn't say that exactly."

"Well, we could issue some subpoenas and find out, couldn't we, Doc? Do you kiss those girls?"

If the witness had thought for a moment he might have realized that no one was going to subpoena any girls to tell about his affairs with them, but MacInroth had riled him. He was angry

72

and confused. He struggled for a moment, and then he said, "Yes, I kiss them sometimes."

"And hug them?"

"Yes, sometimes."

"And touch their breasts?"

"I don't think that's any of your business," the witness snapped.

"You will have to answer the question," said the judge. "But I trust it will be about the last question along this line."

MacInroth said nothing more but waited for his answer. The witness considered for a moment and then admitted, "Maybe I do."

"Well, it isn't maybe, now really, is it?" MacInroth pressed.

"Sometimes it's maybe, sometimes it's yes."

"And you touch their legs too?"

"Sometimes."

"And do you undress them?"

The court interrupted. "I think you can make your point without that," the judge said.

"All right, I guess we can concede that he doesn't undress them. But anyway, Doc, you have had physical intimacies with other girls, other than Ruth Gibson, isn't that true?"

"I'm beginning to think I don't like this word physical intimacies," said Russell aggressively.

"Would you prefer to say that you *necked* with Ruth?"

"That sounds more like it."

"And you neck with other girls?"

"Sometimes."

"Then what you were allowed to do with Ruth Gibson wasn't so unusual for you, was it?"

"I guess not," the witness said cautiously.

"You only did with her what you will do with any girl who will let you, isn't that right?"

"No, that's not right."

"Well, forgive me, I can see that the wording of the question would distress you. But anyway, I believe you have said it was not so unusual; that is, what Ruth let you do to her was not unusual. That is what you said, wasn't it?"

"Not exactly, no," Russell protested.

"All right then. How did you put it?"

"I said I guess she was not so unusual."

"It is not unusual for a girl to let you neck with her?"

"No."

"All right." MacInroth walked back to his table, stood there for a moment looking at his notes, then sat down. His cross-examination had impressed the jury, and now he was affecting a dramatic pause.

"At nine o'clock on the morning of May twentieth, were there other people on the street—lots of people, I mean?" MacInroth asked casually, as though he were starting a new cross-examination and this was his first question.

So intent was the witness on the chain of previous questioning that he was caught not listening, and MacInroth had to repeat the question. In reply Russell said that there might have been people on the street, but he didn't know because he had been in the back of the store until he came out to let Louis in.

"In your experience are there usually people on the street at nine o'clock on a Saturday morning?"

"I would say usually, yes."

"Many people?"

"Considerable."

"It would be unusual for the streets to be vacated at that time of day on Saturday, wouldn't it?"

"Yes, I suppose so."

"How about cars? Was there a car parked in front of DeWitt's?"

"No, the parking places directly in front of the store were vacant."

"All right. Now, let me ask you this: Can you place the date when you say Ruth Gibson first made to you a proposition to rob the store?"

"I am not sure of the day exactly, sir."

"Well, you have said, I believe, that you stopped seeing her about six weeks before the robbery, and you said that you went out with her over a period of about two months. Would that mean that you were seeing her in the months of February and March?"

"That's about right."

"And did you date her frequently during that period?"

"Yes, two or three times a week."

"From about the first of February?"

"Yes, I guess so."

"Well, how long had you been seeing her when she first spoke of taking something from the store?"

"Well, two or three weeks, I suppose."

"Middle of February, along toward the first of March?"

"Yes."

"So you continued to discuss this proposition for about a month before you stopped seeing her?"

"We didn't discuss it. She kept saying we ought to do something like that, and I kept telling her to forget it."

"Well, that kind of talk continued over a period of a month?"

"Yes."

MacInroth was bearing down now as though he were in pursuit of something significant. "And did she bring it up every time you were together?"

"Yes, just about every time."

"So she made the proposition two or three times a week for some four weeks. Would that be about right?"

"Yes." These questions were not bothering the witness, and he shot back his answers. He seemed to think the worst was over and that the lawyer was only fishing again.

"And you say that at first you thought she was only joking?"

"Yes."

"How soon did you become convinced that she was serious?"

"Well, I got the idea gradually. The third or fourth time she brought it up I guess I knew she meant it."

"And what was your reaction to that?"

"To what?"

"Well, when you became convinced she meant it, what did you think? How did you receive the idea?"

"I was worried, concerned. I didn't like the idea at all."

"And you say that toward the end she began to suggest that she could get someone else to commit the robbery for her?"

"Yes, sir."

"And how did you take that?"

"I didn't like that either."

"That worried you?"

"Yes, sir."

"You didn't think she was joking about that?"

"No, sir."

"Well, now tell me, Doc, why did this worry you?"

"Well," said Russell almost indignantly, "that's a pretty serious thing to talk about doing."

"You thought she was capable of it then?"

"Well, yes."

"There would have been no cause for worry if she was not capable of doing it. It would have been just talk. Right?"

"Right."

"So you thought she was serious and you thought she could do it, was capable of it?"

"Yes." Russell was growing cautious now. The lawyer had followed this line too long for it to mean nothing. The witness wanted time to try to figure out where the lawyer was going. MacInroth understood and pressed on so as not to give Russell the time.

"But you continued to date her?" asked MacInroth.

"Well, yes."

"Was that because you were having so much fun with her that the talk of a robbery didn't mean much to you?"

"No, not at all. I thought I could talk her out of it."

"But it turned out that you couldn't. Right?"

"It turned out that I couldn't," agreed Russell.

"Now, Paul," said MacInroth, using that name for the first time, "tell us—when did you first tell Mr. Garfield about these propositions the girl was making to you?" MacInroth arose and moved in front of the witness stand, as though to hear the answer better.

Now Russell knew where the lawyer had been leading him. He sat still for a long moment, looking steadily at MacInroth, and then in a firm voice he said, "I didn't tell him."

"So you are telling us that a young woman—a young woman you believed capable of committing such an act—repeatedly pro-

76

posed that you steal from your employer. *But . . .*" he paused significantly, "you did not tell your employer?" As MacInroth finished his question, his tone was triumphant. The witness had followed him deeper into the trap than he could have hoped.

Russell looked at MacInroth for a long silent moment, and then he said, "Is that a question I'm supposed to answer?"

"Your Honor," said MacInroth, "could we have a few minutes' recess?"

"Well, I wasn't going to take a recess at this time of the afternoon," said the judge, "but I suppose we can if you have some reason."

"I do, your Honor, and I would appreciate it."

"Very well, the court will stand recessed for ten minutes. The jury is admonished again not to discuss the case with anyone."

The witness Paul Russell bolted from the jury box and strode across the floor to Baumgardner and began to talk in an earnest, gesticulating manner. This was not lost on the jurors, who watched him as they ambled out of the box and out toward the hall. Why some people think a trial turns on and off like a television set and that a jury does not notice anything except when the court is in session, is beyond my understanding.

Of course I could see why the witness was disturbed and wanted to talk immediately with the prosecuting attorney. If Paul Russell had been dueling MacInroth with rapiers instead of with words, he would have been bleeding from several long, deep cuts. MacInroth had suggested, and implanted in the minds of the jurors, a motive for Russell to lie—implying that Russell himself was suspected of faking the story of the robbery and that he therefore wanted a conviction in this trial to bolster his story and restore his reputation. It was a weak implication, of course, but Russell had strengthened it himself by lying twice. MacInroth had used a very interesting and usually very effective technique of cross-examination. He actually led the witness into lying. First, he asked Russell if he had heard the rumors that he had committed the robbery himself. Russell could have said that he had heard the rumors, as everyone knew he must have, and he could have added an indignant denial before MacInroth could have gotten in an objection; and if he had, Paul Russell would have won the jury's sympathy, and he would have continued to enjoy their confidence. But for some reason of his own, which MacInroth must have anticipated, he chose to refute the rumors by denying that he had even heard them. He meant only to play them down, aware that MacInroth could probably not prove he had heard them; but he failed to understand that the jury would know perfectly well that he, of all people, could not have failed to hear such talk. When he said he had never heard about it, the jury had to think he was lying. Of course, even without a lawyer's suggestion, a jury is apt to think that a witness who lies about anything will lie about everything. Then the witness fell into a second trap. The jury unquestionably knew that Paul Russell did not confine himself to mere light necking when he parked with a girl on dark country roads in the dead of winter. But that was what he said. Again MacInroth probably anticipated what the witness would say. He knew that when he forced Russell to discuss his sex life he would think the purpose was to picture him as an unsavory character. Actually MacInroth wanted a pious denial. He wanted the witness to claim he engaged only in light necking. The jury would never believe it. *And,* even if Paul Russell were telling the truth—even if he never heard the rumors and never undressed the girl—the jury was still going to think that he had and that he was lying when he said he had not. However, I think, and I imagine most of the jurors thought, that Russell had told two lies. Not very big lies, just little ones about tangential issues, but big enough to shake the confidence of the jury, at least a little.

Just before asking for the recess MacInroth had made a point which he would exploit in argument and which became crucial to the case. I am sure Russell did not realize what a damaging admission he had made. I know, because I discussed it with him, that Baumgardner did not then realize it either. The jury, of course, probably did not catch what neither the witness nor the prosecutor had caught, but when MacInroth later pressed the point repeatedly and forcefully in argument they must have recognized the importance of this one small point. It was this: Russell admitted that he had not told his employer, Garfield, that a girl whose values he doubted had repeatedly proposed he rob the store. The admission damaged Russell's credibility more than all the rest of the cross-examination.

During the recess, then, Russell conferred with Baumgardner. MacInroth and Day conferred with the court reporter, Mrs. Kiggins, taking notes from portions of the testimony which she read to them from her stenotype tape. The two defendants sat at opposite ends of the defense table and did not look at each other. None of the principals, except the judge and the jury, left the room. The recess was short, and before the ten minutes were up, nearly everyone had returned to his place.

MacInroth began a new line of cross-examination by asking, "Doc, does it embarrass you that Mr. Garfield will no longer let you open the safe?"

"I don't know what you mean," said Russell calmly. Plainly he had been instructed to answer each question calmly and courteously. Of course, he had been so instructed before, but he had occasionally forgotten.

"Well, sir, you have been reluctant to admit that you can't open it anymore. Why did you tell us on direct examination that you could open it and then tell us on cross-examination that you couldn't?"

"I don't think I did say that."

"Didn't you tell us, in response to Mr. Baumgardner's question, that you could open the safe?"

"I don't remember saying so."

"All right, I have consulted the stenotype tape. Mrs. Kiggins, will you read the portion of the direct examination I asked for?"

The reporter picked up her tape and began to read in an inevitably sing-song, noncommittal tone. No court stenographer I ever heard could avoid that tone.

"'Question,'" she read. "'Why do you go in at eight-thirty?' Answer: 'Well, sir, I open the store for Mr. Garfield. There is about half an hour's work to do before we open the doors. I don't have any sweeping to do—that's done for us at night. But I usually give the walk a quick once-over. It has butts on it and so forth. Then I get the lights on, unlock the cash register, and open the safe and put the trays of jewelry in the showcase.' Question: 'You have the combination to the safe yourself?' Answer:

'Yes, sir. Only Mr. Garfield has the key to a locked compartment inside the safe, but I can open the main safe.'"

"Thank you, Mrs. Kiggins," said MacInroth. "Now, Doc, when you said you have the combination to the safe, that wasn't exactly true, was it?"

"I was referring to the time of the robbery. I had the combination then."

"Were you confused under direct examination? Did the prosecuting attorney press you too hard or ask you embarrassing questions?"

"No, sir."

"And yet you said, 'I *can* open the main safe.' And you answered, 'Yes, sir,' when you were asked, 'You *have* the combination to the safe yourself?' Are you in the habit of using the present tense when referring to things that happened six months ago?"

"I thought we were talking about things the way they were in May and before that."

"If I asked you what kind of a day May twentieth was, would you say, 'It *is* nice and sunshiny'?"

Russell drew in his breath and let his "No" escape as he exhaled.

"If I asked you about your last Christmas dinner, you wouldn't say, 'I have turkey,' would you?" MacInroth did not wait long for an answer but went on, saying, "And yet, you said, 'I have the combination.'"

"I didn't say that," argued Russell.

"All right. You answered 'Yes' to the question, 'You *have* the combination?' Didn't you?"

"I thought we were talking about things the way they were at the time of the robbery," insisted Russell.

"I didn't ask you that," MacInroth said, shaking his head with his eyes closed. "I asked you if you answered 'Yes' to the question, 'You have the combination?'"

"Well, it's in the record that way, isn't it?"

"Precisely that way. And you also said, 'I *can* open the main safe,' didn't you?"

"That's what the record says."

"But you do not have the combination. And you cannot open the main safe. Isn't that a fact?"

"As of now, it is."

"Thank you. That's all."

The abrupt termination of the cross-examination surprised the witness. He was left staring incredulously at MacInroth, who now leaned back in his chair and clasped his hands comfortably across his belly.

MacInroth had confined the cross-examination entirely to an attack on the credibility of the witness. Baumgardner now rose to rehabilitate Russell's damaged credibility.

"In what circumstances is the safe now opened, Paul?"

Russell relaxed a bit under friendly examination. He crossed his legs. "Mr. Garfield comes in at eight-thirty and opens it himself."

"Then does he stay in the store with you?"

"No, he goes out to get his breakfast, just the way he always did."

"Are you left alone in the store then?"

"Yes."

"Until when?"

"Until the girls come in at nine, or a customer comes in, or Mr. Garfield comes back. It depends on the day."

"Does he leave the safe open?"

"Yes."

"So, even though you do not open the door of the safe, you are left alone in the store for half an hour or more with it open and with all the contents available to you?"

"Yes."

"Okay. That's all."

The judge looked at MacInroth, who shook his head. The judge said, "That will be all. You can go."

Paul Russell rose and walked from the room, apparently a little shaken at the manner in which his tenure on the witness stand had so suddenly ended. The jurors turned their heads and watched him leave.

The cross-play of belief and disbelief in a trial is fascinating to watch. It is impossible to measure, of course, but one can speculate about it. At the end of direct examination Russell undoubtedly stood high in the estimation of the jury, as he did in that of all the listeners. Everyone believed him. After his cross-examination, no one could be quite sure. That is the purpose of cross-examination, as everyone understands. Rarely does a witness collapse under cross-examination and admit he has been lying. Men are too brazen for that, and cross-examiners are hardly ever that good. The cross-examiner's job is to substitute uncertainty for certainty. In a criminal trial, if the defense can cause uncertainty in the jury it has done its job and should win its acquittal, because it is fundamental that the state must prove its case *beyond a reasonable doubt.* Reasonable doubt is an elusive concept; lawyers have tried to define it without much success, and it must mean very different things to different jurors and different juries, in spite of our attempts to reduce it to a comprehensible formula. How much doubt is a reasonable doubt? How much certainty is enough for conviction? How much uncertainty is enough for acquittal? During the presentation of the state's case the prosecution must try to manufacture certainty, and the defense must hinder that effort by substituting uncertainty wherever the prosecution leaves an opening. If the jury had decided the case at this point, would the testimony of Paul Russell have convicted Roger Louis and Ruth Gibson? Some people in town that evening thought it should have, and some people thought it should not, and I suppose the same division existed among the jurors.

Anyway, Russell's testimony and the cross-examination created certainty in the minds of some and uncertainty in the minds of others. Of course the matter of degree further complicates the pattern. Now, to the complexity created by the performance of this one witness we add the complexity to be created by the performance of another, and then another. Eventually, the trial becomes kaleidoscopic and defies analysis. But am I saying it becomes irrational? Or is that a proper question? For, after all, what is rationality? To reason at all it is necessary to reason about something, and where do we find the facts about which we reason? In the kaleidoscope of experience, undoubtedly. And from myriad related complexities of facts available to us, we select some and combine them into patterns of logic. Which is what a jury must do. From all the words spoken, all the impressions gained, all the facts established, all the prejudices brought into the courtroom and all the new ones created by being present at the trial—from all this and more the jurors must select a few manageable facts, impressions, and ideas, and reason about them until they reach a rational conclusion. Who knows what word, what nuance of tone, what facial expression, or anything at all a juror will select and use as one of the reduced number of ideas with which he chooses to reason? He cannot use everything he has in his mind. That would be unmanageable. Undoubtedly his mental process is one of selection. He will reduce the unmanageable complex to the manageable, a process of simplification. The trial lawyer must try to make certain points stand out so that the juror will select *them* in his process of simplification.

Lives and trials are not unlike. Our senses bring us far too many impressions to manage and comprehend. We all select; we have to. If we did not, the world would be like the kaleidoscope, shifting in irrational and beautiful meaningless shapes. Man can enjoy that kind of world momentarily, but he cannot live in it, not so long as the curse of Adam requires that he feed and clothe and house himself. So we must make patterns where there are none, try to introduce certainty where none exists, learn to anticipate the future and have confidence in it as though we really could know what will happen one minute from now, instead of only guessing. To do that, like the jurors we pick and choose the impressions we can combine into logical patterns, and we reject as false those which do not fit into the concepts we make for ourselves.

The universe is wide. We reject too much of it. We deprive ourselves of too much of it. We ignore the way the world is because so much of it does not fit into our ideas of how it must be.

But I am supposed to be writing about a trial.

IV

T HE PROSECUTION called its second witness, Garson Jackson, the chief of police of the City of Alexandria. Jackson is only twenty-nine, and some of the older members of the force dislike him intensely for that reason and no other. His father was chief of police many years ago, and Garson joined the force as soon as he completed his service in the Marine Corps. He is chief because his father was, but also because he is obviously dedicated to the Alexandria Police as a lifetime career. For a policeman, his intelligence is impressive, and he is a big, tough fellow who looks good in the uniform. Until he married several years ago, half a dozen girls were chasing him all the time. Since he is a young chief and since he is handsome and smart and appealing to women, his overconfidence is inevitable, I suppose, but it is his only fault I can see. People who know him better than I probably see others.

Garson Jackson strode purposefully across the front of the courtroom as if he intended to imply that crime is serious. The clerk had to be called in to administer the oath to him, because he had not been in the courtroom when the other witnesses were sworn.

"What is your name, address, and occupation?" asked the prosecuting attorney when the witness had been sworn.

"Garson T. Jackson, 231 Elm Street, Alexandria, Ohio. I am the chief of police of the City of Alexandria."

"And you have been chief of police . . . "

"For a year and a half." Garson could anticipate the questions; he had been a witness before. Besides, he enjoyed the role and had undoubtedly rehearsed what he would say. Because he is an ex-marine he wears a khaki uniform in the summer, unlike the gray uniform worn by other policemen, with trousers pressed to a sharp straight crease and shirt pegged to fit snugly around the waist. He wears the gold badge the city once presented his father for years of service. Usually he keeps his shirt open at the neck, but today for his appearance in court he was wearing a khaki tie to match his shirt. I was glad he had not worn his gun belt.

"Were you in headquarters the morning when the call came in about the robbery at DeWitt's Jewelry Store?"

"Yes, I was. That call was logged at nine-eleven A.M., on Saturday, May 20, 1961."

"Did you take the call?"

"No, it was taken by Corporal Middleton."

"Who responded to the call?"

"I did. I took Patrolman Gerald Pierce with me."

"What did you do when you arrived at the store?"

"We ascertained that the suspect had escaped. When we learned that he had escaped in a car, we took a description of that car and of him and the name of the girl who was with him, and we put that on the air and notified the sheriff and the Highway Patrol to be on the lookout for the car and suspects. Then we went into the store and examined the premises."

"Did you look for fingerprints?"

"Not at that time. I directed Patrolman Pierce to guard the door and not permit anyone to enter or to touch anything. We dusted for fingerprints later, but we were not able to get any distinct impression."

"Did you question Paul Russell?"

"We did."

"What did he tell you?"

"Objection. It is hearsay," said MacInroth, who was still leaning back in his chair with his hands clasped across his belly.

"It will be sustained," said Judge Kemp.

"Did Paul Russell give you a full account of what had happened?"

"Yes."

"Can you describe his demeanor? That is to say, was he nervous? Upset?"

"Yes, he was. Very upset. His hands shook."

"Thank you. That is all."

Bob Day pulled his chair under the table and drew himself closer to his notes. "You say you found no fingerprints?" he asked.

"No, I would say we found too many. The handle of the door, which was the only thing reported to us that the robber touched, bore many impressions, none distinct."

"It had not been wiped off then?"

"No."

"Did you inquire up and down the street to find out whether anyone else had seen this car parked in front of Ted's Men's Shop or this alleged robber enter the store?"

"Yes, I spent some time talking to people up and down the street on both sides."

"Did you find anyone else who saw either the car or the alleged robber?"

"No one had any distinct recollection of it."

"How long afterward did you do this asking?"

"The same morning. I went around that same morning."

"And no one remembered seeing the car or the robber?"

"No."

"Thank you," said Day, ending his cross-examination.

Baumgardner asked, "Did anyone say he had been watching?"

"No, they all said they just couldn't remember seeing anything."

"In other words, did anyone deny that the car was parked where Russell said it was or that a man entered the store as he said he did?"

"No, no one could say yes or no."

"Thank you. That's all."

Garson Jackson rose and walked to the door.

"Call Nathan Garfield," said Joe Baumgardner.

Quentin the bailiff went out into the hall loudly calling the name of the next witness. Mr. Garfield returned with him.

Nathan Garfield bought DeWitt's Jewelry Store during the Great Depression. I suppose his name is not really Garfield but something longer and Polish, for he is one of several sons his father and mother brought across the water with them about the turn of the century. These Polish Jews did not come to America poor, and they did not come rich, either. They came with a little money and a great deal of talent and ambition, settled in Pittsburgh and established themselves in business. I have seen the old man, the father, who brought his sons to America. He came here with Nathan in 1932 to look at the store and the community and to decide if it was a good business and a good place to invest some of the Garfield money. They decided it was. Nathan and his wife moved here and took over the old store. People in Alexandria expected the reputable name of DeWitt's to become the front for a shoddy credit jewelry store, but they were wrong. Nathan had some ideas about how the business could be improved by modernization of methods and facilities, but he kept it solid and respectable. The community accepted him and his family and then learned to like him. Today hardly any businessman in town is better liked than Nathan Garfield. He is a thin, slight man whose crop of fine white hair makes a striking contrast with his dark complexion. He has a hooked nose of the sort which is called Semitic and probably is, though it is out of fashion today to speak of people's racial characteristics.

Nathan was the most hesitant and nervous of the witnesses who had so far appeared. He sat down in the witness chair and looked about him as though trapped, and looked to his townsmen for sympathy.

Joe Baumgardner rose to his feet for the questioning of Nathan Garfield. "Mr. Garfield, will you state your full name, please?"

"My name is Nathan Louis Garfield," replied the witness.

"And you live in Alexandria?"

"I do. Since 1932."

"And you are the owner of DeWitt's Jewelry Store, or DeWitt's Jewelry Company?"

"Yes. The store is called DeWitt's Jewelry Store. It is owned by the DeWitt Jewelry Company, and I am the owner of all of the stock of the DeWitt Jewelry Company, which I bought from the DeWitt estate in 1932."

"Do you employ Paul Russell in your store?"

"Yes, he has worked for me for the past several years."

"Was he employed in your store at the time when it was robbed?"

"Yes."

"When was that?"

"That was on May twentieth of this year."

"Where were you when the robbery occurred?"

"I was having breakfast at Morton's."

"Is that your custom?"

"Yes, I have done that for years. I have coffee and a roll for breakfast and read the papers and chat with my friends. Every morning."

"Is it your custom to let Paul Russell open the store for you?"

"Yes, it is. I stop by and then go on out to have my breakfast, and Paul opens the store."

"How long has Paul Russell worked for you?"

"Well, it has been five years now, I think. He worked for me part time before that, before he was in military service, when he was in high school."

"During that time have you ever before suffered any loss by theft?"

"No, never."

"Any unexplained loss of cash or merchandise?"

"No. Well, wait," Nathan Garfield hastily corrected himself. "Once a young boy who was looking at a ring ran out the door with it. My daughter was waiting on him, and he took the ring and ran out the door. I saw him myself."

"That's all?"

"Yes, I have never had an insurance claim. We recovered the ring the same day. The police caught the young man easily enough."

"Mr. Garfield, what was the value of the jewelry taken in the robbery?"

"Wholesale, thirty-one hundred dollars."

"How did you first learn of the robbery?"

"One of the boys from Ted's Men's Shop came and got me at Morton's."

"I believe that is all. Thank you."

Bob Day whispered something to MacInroth and then asked, "Mr. Garfield, I think Paul Russell said you stop in at the store first and then go to Morton's for breakfast. Isn't that a change in your habits?"

"No, I don't think so."

"Well, didn't you used to go directly to Morton's without stopping by the store?"

Nathan Garfield thought about that for a moment and then said, "Yes, now that you mention it, I did do it that way for a while."

"And why do you have to stop by the store first now?"

"Well, I open the safe so Paul can put the merchandise out in the showcases."

"Didn't you keep the safe locked before?"

"Yes, but Paul could open it himself."

"But he can't now?"

"No, I changed the combination. I do that every few years."

"When was the combination changed?"

"Shortly after the robbery."

"I see. Has any of the stolen jewelry been recovered?"

"No, none of it."

"Was it the sort of thing which could be identified and recovered?"

"Most of it was, yes."

"When did you first learn that Ruth Gibson made several propositions to Paul Russell that he help her steal from your store?"

"I learned of that when he told the police about it."

"Had you known he was going out with her?"

"No."

"Thank you, Mr. Garfield. That's all."

Nathan Garfield remained seated in the witness box, and the judge had to tell him he could leave.

"Might I stay in the courtroom and watch the trial now?" he asked.

"Yes," said the judge. "You have been excused as a witness, so you can stay."

Nathan Garfield found the swinging gate in the rail and went to the rear of the courtroom.

"Call George Ballentine," said the prosecutor.

The sheriff had been waiting to testify, and he hardly let Quentin open the door to call him before he ducked around the bailiff and headed for the stand. He had been sworn in the clerk's office, he told the judge, and he was ready to testify. As I mentioned before, George is a bald-headed man. He wears spectacles and a hearing aid, and I suppose he looks less like a sheriff than anyone in the state. He does a good job, though, and was re-elected by a bigger vote than he received in the first election. Potential lawbreakers seem to be afraid of him, and big men surrender meekly and come along when he beckons. His reputation says he will use his gun because he is so little and so nervous that he would draw his gun and shoot rather than try to subdue a felon with fists or blackjack. I have never heard of a case where he actually did it, but there must have been one, because they talk about him respectfully in the bars around the county, and when he walks in to break up a drunken brawl, the brawlers separate on command. George ran for sheriff because he was not making a living as a farmer and because people assured him he could beat the incumbent. He was defeated the first time he ran, but the next time he reaped the reward of having campaigned the entire four years between elections. He has a lot of political sense. The hill people like him.

"State your full name, please," said Joe Baumgardner.

"George Ballentine."

"You are the sheriff of this county?"

"That's right."

"How long have you been sheriff?"

"I was elected in 1956."

"I will direct your attention to May 20, 1961, and ask you if you were in your office when a call came in reporting a robbery at DeWitt's Jewelry Store?"

"I was in the office, and that call come in about nine-thirty. It come in from the city police. They said they'd had this robbery, and the robber had escaped in a light green Chevrolet, and he had a girl called Ruth Gibson with him. They wanted us to check the county roads and around and see if we could find that car. They give us a description of the fellow they wanted."

"What did you do?"

"Well, the only thing I knowed to do was go out and see the Gibsons, if it was their daughter in the car, and see if I could find out who she might be with."

"Did you go to the Gibsons'?"

"Well, no, not right away. I had two summonses to serve, and we've only got four cars, and those summonses went out the same way, so I waited for the girl to get them ready so I could take them and serve them on the way."

"What time did you leave the office?"

"It was about ten or a quarter after. As best I can recall."

"Did you go alone?"

"No, I took Mike with me. Mike Bradstreet—he's a deputy, you know. I took him in the car with me."

"Where did you go?"

"Well, the Gibsons live out on County Road Five. I had to check around the courthouse to find out where they live. I'd never been to their place before. One of the summonses went down to Bucknell, so I went there first and let Mike run in and give the man his summons, and then I drove on out Five and dropped the other summons off at a house out there. Then we went on out the road to get to the Gibson place. It's quite a ways out."

"What time did you arrive at the Gibson home?"

"Well, I expect it was after eleven before we got out there. You know, that's a gravel road up there on the hill and pretty twisty. Then when you get to their place you can't drive in. You have to walk up over the hill. It was pretty muddy, too."

"Who did you talk to?"

"Well, I talked to a couple of the kids at first and got them to go in the house and bring their father out. He come out, and so did their mother."

"That would be Joel and Mary Gibson?"

"That's right. That's their names."

"Did you find out from them where their daughter would be?"

"No. They said they hadn't seen her for two weeks but they supposed she'd be in town at the place where she rooms, either there or at work. So I asked them what fellows she ran around with. They give me the names of two or three fellows they thought she had been out with. So we let it go at that and went back down to the car."

"Then what did you do?"

"Well, me and Mike sat in the car for a while and tried to figure out where to go next. We talked about the names of the fellows the Gibsons had gave us, and we remembered that the Louises, one or the other family of them, had a boy about her age or so. We tried to remember what sort of a looking fellow he was, and we thought we could picture him, so he seemed to sort of fit the description we had. After that we decided to go see the Louises and see what they had to say."

"Was Roger Louis one of the names the Gibsons had given you?"

"Sure, didn't I say?"

"All right. Go on."

"Okay. Well, we went looking for Louises then, and the nearest ones to where we were was the family of Ben Louis that lives up on Barber's Run. We drove to his house, and there wasn't anybody home but the kids, but they told us they had a cousin named Roger and that he was a son of Jack Louis that lives on the old river road, so we went to see Jack Louis."

"What time was it when you got to his place?"

"Well, it was a lot of driving around, and I expect it was about noon or after. We stopped at a store on the way and picked up some Cokes and a package of cookies to eat. Anyway, Jack Louis was home, and we talked to him about the boy. Asked him what kind of car the boy had, and he said a green 1950 Chevy. He said the boy hadn't been around in a couple of days. He showed us a picture of the boy in his army uniform. He wanted to know

92

if the boy was in trouble, of course, and we said maybe he was and to call us if he came home. Then we went back to the car and called in on the radio and said we figured Roger Louis might be the boy they were looking for, so they could give that to the police, you know."

"All right. Then what did you do?"

"Well, we sat in the car again and talked about where they might have gone. We figured they could have gone for West Virginia or they might have gone toward one of the cities, or they might be trying to hide out somewhere in the hills here in the county. Well, if they went to West Virginia or took off on one of the highways for somewhere else, that was none of our problem. If they were hiding out in the country, that was our problem. So where in the county might they go?"

The sheriff is one of those people who has a lot of saliva in his mouth, and to clear it off the top of his tongue, where it would interfere with conversation, he presses his tongue from time to time against the roof of his mouth. As he does he makes two little clicking sounds, one with the front of his tongue and the other with the back of it. After every couple of sentences he does it, and it goes *tsi-kuh*. Speech mannerisms fascinate me, and people who go *tsi-kuh* have one of the most amusing. You don't dare make fun of a thing like that. I made the mistake once of asking the court reporter if she was taking George's clicks, and she said, no, *tsi-kuh*, she wasn't and what did I mean anyway? I hadn't noticed she did it too.

Some of the sheriff's testimony might have been subject to objection by the defense, but neither of the two attorneys said anything. They had heard George testify often enough to know he was not going to say anything really prejudicial, and they also knew that to object too often can irritate the jury, especially when a popular witness is telling an interesting story. George sat cross-legged, but he was not relaxed. It was work for him to dredge up out of his memory everything he thought the prosecuting attorney might want him to tell. I know that George feels it is not fair to rehearse testimony mentally before the trial and to know ahead of time what you will say, so he was telling his story fresh.

"Well, this is a big county, and there are hundreds of places where a man might hide out. We couldn't check every place. But I remembered that Jack Louis's brother, Sherman Louis, had an old house up on Shambles Ridge about as far from any place as you could get. He doesn't live there any more since he went to work at the plant, so we decided to check up there. We drove up to Shambles Ridge. That's only a township road up there, and the road is broke up pretty bad, but we noticed there was fresh tracks through the mudholes, so somebody was out there on the ridge. Anyway, we come to the place."

"What time was that, do you know?"

"Pretty close to one o'clock. The old house sits up on a hill above the road, and there's a woods up on the hill higher above that. There's just a couple of tracks goes up to the house, and it was too growed up for a car to get up to the house. But there was a car in the tracks, driven in as far as you could get, and it was a green 1950 Chevy.

"Well, if this fellow was supposed to have used a gun we figured we could use help, so we drove on past the place and on around the curve in the road out of sight, and I radioed in for another car. Then Mike and I got out of the car and walked back toward the place. Well, we snuck around some, trying to see who was in the house, and we took a look at the car, and we tried to work our way up the edge of the road toward the house. Then all of a sudden we hear the back door slam, and we could see the fellow and the girl take out across the back and run into the woods."

"Who did you see?"

"Well, at that point we didn't know yet." George had some experience as a witness and was trying to follow what he conceived to be the rules. "It was a fellow in jeans and a white shirt and a girl in shorts. We hollered at them to stop, but they didn't, so we run after them. We could see them going through the brush up there. It wasn't too thick yet that time of year. Mike and I run around the house and followed them up the hill. It's pretty steep, and we could see them up there, scrambling up the hill."

"Did you shout to them to stop? Did you fire your gun?"

Baumgardner interrupted. He was following the story so intently that he had lost the lead to the sheriff. The courtroom was quiet, with everyone listening.

"Yes, we hollered at them all the time to stop, and I fired a warning shot in the air, but they kept on going as best they could. Pretty soon they got to the top, and the girl dropped off and laid down on the ground beside an old log and in some bushes. She thought she could hide that way, but we could see her from where we were. So we just ran right up and caught her easy. Mike kept on going, but I stopped with her for a minute. I put my handcuffs on her ankles so she couldn't run off, and then I went on after Mike and the boy. He'd got out of our sight when he went over the top of the hill, and when I caught up with Mike, he'd stopped and was looking and listening. We couldn't hear him going, and so we figured they'd both made it up to stop and hide, so we started looking into every thick clump of brush around there. Well, to make a long story short, we looked and didn't find him, and while we were doing that he got away from us. Finally we went on down the other side of the hill and we could see where he'd crossed the run down at the bottom. He had quite a start on us then, so we guessed we'd better go back to the car and get on the radio and tell the office what happened. Well, I told Mike to go down to the car and radio, and I'd search the house. I went and got the girl."

"Had she tried to escape?"

"Well, she'd hopped down the hill some and was sitting in a clump of brush. She was just sitting there crying when I got to her. I took her back to the house with me and hooked her onto the bedstead so she wouldn't run away, and then I searched the house."

"What did you find?"

"Nothing. I looked around considerable. So did Mike. And later we really took the place apart. All we found was some clothes of hers and some of his, and some beer and food."

"Is the house furnished?"

"Well, partly. I guess Sherman Louis took all his good stuff out of the house when he moved away. There was a big bed and some chairs and tables, that's about all. There's just a big living room and a bedroom and a kitchen. No water, no electricity, no gas."

"Would it have required a key to get in?"

"No. Anybody could get in. I judge others have used it too."

"Now, Sheriff, while you were there in the house, did Ruth Gibson talk to you?"

"Yes, she did."

"Tell us about that."

"Well, when I got her back to the house I asked her if her name wasn't Ruth Gibson."

"What did she say to that?"

"She said she wasn't. I said I thought she was, and she said she wasn't again. I asked her what her name was, but she wouldn't tell me. She said she wanted to see a lawyer and she wouldn't tell me anything till she saw one. I said, 'Well, I know what your name is. It's Ruth Gibson.' She said, 'No it ain't.' So I let it go. I asked her who the fellow was, and she said she wouldn't say. I asked her what they was doing in the house, and she said she wouldn't tell me. So I give up trying to ask her anything."

"Did she say anything to you on the way back to town in the car?"

"Yes. She said to us a couple times, 'You're going to send me away, aren't you?' or 'You're going to send me up, won't you?' And she said, 'How did you know we was there? How did you know where to look for us?' And she asked us how long we thought she'd get."

"She asked you how long you thought she'd get?"

"Yes, she meant how long a sentence she'd get."

"Now, we'll object to that," said Bob Day suddenly but quietly. "That's only his interpretation of what she meant."

"Sustained. The jury will ignore the witness's interpretation of the meaning of the conversation and will regard only the words the witness says she spoke."

"Did she specifically ask how long a sentence you thought she would get?" asked Joe Baumgardner, betraying a slight impatience. "Tell us what words she used about that."

"Well," said the sheriff, rubbing his chin and wriggling in his chair, "she said, 'I suppose they'll send me away, won't they? How long do you think I'll get?'"

"Then what did she say?"

"Well, I told her I thought she'd get ten years, and then she got all hysterical and cried the rest of the way back to town."

"When you got back to town what did you do?"

"Well, I turned her over to my wife to put her in the jail, and then Mike and me went back out in the car to look for the boy. We'd called all the cars out by radio, and we were covering all the roads around Shambles Ridge. We'd just got out of town when we got a radio call that one of the cars had picked up Roger Louis walking on the road out there, so we went back to the house and looked some more, and I had Mike drive the Chevrolet in."

"When you returned to the office, did your deputies have Roger Louis in custody?"

"Yes. They had him in a cell, and we was ready to question him."

"Did he cooperate with you?"

"Well, he said he wouldn't talk to us before he seen a lawyer. He said he wanted to call his father and have him get a lawyer. We kept on about it for a while, but he wouldn't say anything but that. So we let him make his call and then we put him back in jail, and we got the girl out again and tried to talk to her. Same thing."

"Did she admit she was Ruth Gibson?"

"No. She just said she wanted to see a lawyer too. So we let her make a call, and she called her boss. I mean she called Billy Reitlinger. Then we locked her up again. We had called the city, of course, and told them who we had, and Garson Jackson come down to the courthouse, and he went across the street and got Russell and brought him back."

"Describe what you did then."

"Well, I got a couple of prisoners out of the jail and a couple of fellows that was hanging around the courthouse, and we lined them up in the hall outside the office and put Roger Louis in the line with them, and when Russell come in we asked him if the man who robbed him was there. He pointed to Louis and said, 'That's the man there.' He didn't have no hesitation about it."

Baumgardner stood up and asked, "Is the man Paul Russell identified as Roger Louis in the courtroom now?"

"Sure," said the sheriff. "That's him setting there beside Mr. MacInroth."

"Did you then ask Russell to identify Ruth Gibson?"

"Yes. We took him back to the jail where she was, and he looked at her and said she was Ruth Gibson."

"Is the girl you arrested on Shambles Ridge and who was identified by Paul Russell as Ruth Gibson in the courtroom now?"

"That's her right there," the sheriff said, pointing at the girl sitting beside Bob Day. He smiled at her, and his chest trembled as he laughed silently.

Through all of the sheriff's testimony about her capture, Ruth Gibson had kept looking steadily at him. The bailiff told me later that she was smiling at him most of the time, not a big smile, but a quizzical little smile, an embarrassed smile perhaps. I could see the face of Roger Louis. He held his head down and looked up toward the witnesses by rolling his eyes up beneath his brows.

"What," asked Baumgardner, "did Ruth Gibson say to Paul Russell when he identified her in the jail?"

"She said, 'I might have known you'd have something to do with it. It's the sort of thing you'd do.'"

"Did either Roger Louis or Ruth Gibson ever give you a statement?"

"No."

"Thank you. That's all."

Bob Day conducted the cross-examination of the sheriff. His first question was, "Sheriff, when Paul Russell identified Roger Louis in your lineup outside your office, did Louis say anything when Russell pointed to him?"

"Yes, he said Russell was crazy, he'd never seen Russell before."

"How many men besides Roger Louis did you have in that lineup?"

"I believe there was four others."

"Do you remember who they were?"

"No, not all of them. Some of them I do."

"Sheriff, if you were describing Roger Louis, how would you describe him?"

"I'd say he's about five foot ten, average build, dark-complected, dark brown hair, brown eyes, about twenty-five to thirty years old."

"What kind of description did the city police give you when you went out looking for the green Chevrolet with the man and the girl in it?"

"About the same."

"In other words, the description they received from Paul Russell and gave you was of a man about five feet ten inches tall, with dark complexion and brown hair and eyes, average build? Is that right?"

"That's right," the sheriff agreed.

"Among these other four men you had in your lineup, were there any with dark brown hair?"

The sheriff pursed his lips and took his chin between his fingers and considered for a moment. "Well," he said, "we just used the men we had handy around there that day. I don't guess any of them had just exactly dark brown hair, though, now that you mention it."

"Was one of them bald?"

"Well, yes, one of them was. I guess another one was, too, sort of."

"Were any of them fat?"

"Yes, sir. We had old Dick Dusey who works as a janitor in the courthouse, and I guess you'd say he's pretty fat," the sheriff laughed.

"Yes," Day agreed. "I guess you would say he is. Then, how about the two who had been in jail, did they look pretty seedy? Unshaven, I mean? Like they had just been brought unexpectedly out of the jail?"

"Yes, they did look that way. They were a couple of drunks we had."

"Isn't it a fact then, Sheriff, that the only man you had in the lineup who was about five feet ten, dark-haired, with dark complexion and brown eyes, was Roger Louis?"

"Yes, that's about right."

"Well, then," said Bob Day triumphantly, "it couldn't have been much of a surprise to you when Russell picked out Roger Louis, could it?"

"I wasn't surprised, no," said the sheriff in the same patient, helpful way in which he had couched all his testimony.

"Roger Louis was the only man you had in the lineup who even vaguely resembled the man whose description you had been given, wasn't he?" Day pressed on.

"That's right," said the sheriff in a manner and voice which suggested he had just learned something new about the business of being a sheriff.

"And Paul Russell, having described the kind of man he had described, could not have picked anyone else out of that lineup, could he?"

"I don't suppose so."

"Now, Sheriff, I would like to take up something else," said Bob Day. He got up for the first time and walked over beside the jury box to be closer to his witness. "When you searched the house on Shambles Ridge, what were you looking for?"

"The missing money and jewelry."

"And a gun?"

"Well, yes. A gun too."

"Did you find any of those things?"

"No."

"And did you search the car?"

"Yes, and didn't find anything."

"When Louis and Ruth Gibson ran out of the back of the house, were they carrying anything?"

"No, not that I could see."

"How was Louis dressed?"

"Well, he was kind of far off, but I judged he was wearing a pair of blue jeans and a white shirt."

"What was he wearing when you next saw him, that is when he was brought in to your office?"

"A pair of blue jeans and a white shirt."

"Did you find a blue jacket in the house or car or anywhere you looked?"

"No."

"Would you judge that Louis could have carried much jewelry or money or a gun in the pockets of his jeans?"

"Not very much, no. The pockets aren't very big."

"How about Ruth Gibson? How was she dressed?"

"Well, she had on a pair of shorts made out of blue jeans by cutting the legs off, and a white shirt."

"You say you found some clothes of hers and some of his in the house. What items were those?"

"Well, there was some underclothes, his and hers. And there was a sweater of hers and a sweatshirt of his. And there was a black skirt of hers and a pair of black pants of his. And there was a cap of his. I think that's all."

"How much might she have been carrying in her pockets when she ran out of the house?"

"Nothing, I don't think. There wasn't no pocket in her shirt, and she'd cut the pockets off the jeans she'd cut down for shorts."

"And it is a fact, isn't it, that you have never found any of the stolen property?"

"That's right. Never found any of it."

"Did you find the gun used in the robbery?"

"No."

"Did you search the Louis family home?"

"Yes, we did."

"But you didn't find anything there either?"

"No."

"Now, Sheriff, going back to the point on the hill when you captured Ruth Gibson. Did you tell her what she was being arrested for?"

"No, I just grabbed her. She knowed she was under arrest."

"Had you shouted at the two of them why you wanted them to stop?"

"No."

"While you were putting your handcuffs on Ruth, did you talk to her at all?"

"I told her I was doing that to see to it she didn't run off."

"Is that all you said?"

"Yes."

"When you came back to her did you then tell her why you were arresting her?"

"I figured she knew."

"But did you tell her?"

"No."

"When you had her in the house, did you say anything to her about the robbery?"

"No, she wouldn't even tell me her name, so I didn't tell her anything either."

"Did she ask you why you were arresting her?"

"No, she didn't ask."

"In the car, did you then talk about the robbery?"

"No."

"When did you first tell her what charge you were holding her for?"

"I never told her."

"When did she first find out?"

"I suppose she knew all along."

"You *suppose* so. But when did she first hear you say anything which would tell her?"

"Well," said the sheriff, and he stopped to think for a moment, "I guess maybe we didn't in so many words tell her what she would be charged with until we got her in the office, and I said to Chloe there in the office, I said, 'Here's the girl that's wanted for the robbery. We got her.' And I said something about the police would be glad to hear we got her. I guess that's the first time any of us said in so many words that's what she was charged with."

"Up to that time, had you said anything else to her about the robbery?"

"No, I guess not. I was kind of mad because she wouldn't tell us her name, so we didn't talk much on the way back in the car, or while we was searching the house either."

"Now, Sheriff, let's talk about an if. If the girl had not committed the robbery, if she was not with someone who did, then in your office when you spoke to the office girl was the first time she would know what she was charged with. Right?"

"Objection," Baumgardner said tentatively and without much conviction.

"Never mind," said the judge. "You may answer."

"Well," the sheriff said thoughtfully, "I suppose that's right."

"What's right? Will you state it in full, please?"

"Well," said the sheriff, picking his words, "if she didn't do it, then maybe she wouldn't have known what she was arrested for until we got in there and I said that. But she said. . . ."

"Thank you," Bob cut him off. "It is possible, then, isn't it, Sheriff, that her talk about what sentence she would get did not refer to a sentence for armed robbery?"

"What else could she have been talking about?" asked the sheriff ingenuously.

"We'll find out maybe," said Bob Day, nodding his head. "But for all you had said to her, she could have been referring to something else, couldn't she?"

"For all I said to her, yes," admitted the sheriff.

"And for all Mike said to her?"

"Yes."

"Now then, when in the office Ruth Gibson heard you say for the first time that she had been arrested for robbery, what was her reaction?"

"She started to cry again."

"Was she hysterical?"

"I guess you'd say she was, yes."

"And then you put her in jail?"

"Well, she wasn't that hysterical. She didn't need a doctor or anything."

"All right, but the point is, that ended the conversation, didn't it?"

"Yes, I guess it did."

"And the next time you talked to her was when?"

"That was after we had been out and searched the house again and brought the Chevy in, and after we had tried to question Louis."

"How long a period of time elapsed between the time you put Ruth Gibson in jail and the time you took her out to question her again?"

"Oh, a couple of hours, anyway. It was getting pretty late in the day by then."

"And that was when she asked to see a lawyer?"

"Yes, and we let her make her phone call."

"But she had had two hours to regain her composure and to think of asking for a lawyer?"

"Yes."

"All right. That's all. Thank you."

As Bob Day walked back to his seat Joe Baumgardner rose. When Bob Day was seated, Joe asked, "Sheriff, did Ruth Gibson at any time say anything to you to suggest that she thought she was being arrested for anything other than armed robbery?"

"No, she didn't."

"Okay. That's all."

Sheriff George Ballentine pushed himself up by grasping the rail of the witness box. He adjusted his spectacles on his nose, looked around to see if anyone had anything else to say to him, and then walked toward the door.

"Since it is ten after four, this is probably the best time to recess for the day," said Judge Kemp. "I want to admonish the jury not to speak to anyone about this trial. You should not read the newspaper account of it. You should not make up your mind about it until you have heard it all. The court will be in recess until nine tomorrow morning."

V

WHEN HENRY RECESSED the trial, the participants and the spectators scattered in every direction. Quentin looked dismayed. He always wanted to hold the people in their places while the judge walked out with dignity, but I never did it that way, nor does Henry Kemp. We never have been tied to formality in our court here in Marshall County, not since I was judge. I always thought a judge should find his dignity in what he does and not in the artificial solemnities of the gavel and the robe. I was wrong about that, but by the time I found it out it was too late to change it. People should not feel at home in court. They should be awed a little, and if it takes robes and wigs and show to awe them, then we should use robes and wigs and show. Our work in court is justice; justice should be an awesome concept only one step below God, and people should approach the task of justice with reverence and dedication. A little ritual to create the right atmosphere and set it apart from the ordinary tasks of daily life is beneficial. Democracy does not belong in the courtroom. What the people want and think should not count.

Let their wishes count in making the laws, but not in applying them. I was too much the democrat when I was a young judge. Not that I surrendered to popular passions, I don't mean that, but I thought the people should regard the courts as their own, as they consider the legislature their own. I was wrong, but I set the style for our court, and Henry Kemp has not tried to change it. I wish he would.

Judge Kemp stepped down from the bench and came over and stood beside me. Bill Mullen moved to rise from his chair so Henry could sit beside me, but Henry waved and Bill stayed in his seat. Henry Kemp is a rather handsome man, erect and thin and well dressed, with black hair turning gray at the temples. That graying at the temples is an asset for a lawyer or a doctor; it makes any boob look distinguished. It never happened to me. I turned white all over, evenly, and not until I was in my sixties. When I was young I looked young and wished I could look old so people would have more confidence in me. Now that I am old I know there is no reason for people to have confidence in other people only because they are old, and I look back with renewed resentment on the fools who lacked confidence in me when I was young because I was young. I must be careful not to wander like a senile old man. I was saying that Judge Kemp came and stood beside me.

"Any comments, Judge?" he asked me. He was inviting me to criticize his rulings from the bench if I wanted to, which of course I would not have done even if I wanted to.

"No, none at all," I said.

He nodded and turned to look at the crowd leaving the courtroom.

I was interested in the Louis family, now that I knew who they were. The sheriff's recital about Ben and Sherman and Jack Louis reminded me of the structure of the clan, and now I recognized Jack and Ben in the courtroom. Roger left his attorney without a word when the judge recessed for the day, and now he was standing beside his father in the rear of the room. The older man was doing the talking. I had seen his father in court before, and his uncles Ben and Sherm. They had all been in jail from time to time. Sherm served a sentence in the Ohio Penitentiary for larceny one time. I sentenced him. Ben has been on probation for nonsupport two or three times, and I remember threatening to send him to the pen. Jack, the boy's father, was not as familiar to me, though I do remember him in court as a witness in some divorce case or other. I am told that all of them have been jailed by the Municipal Court of Alexandria for drunkenness and disorderly behavior. They are not a pretty family. On the other hand, they own several nice pieces of farmland, some of it not hill land but bottom land and arable, and they work hard between sprees. I supposed, from the looks of what I had seen in the courtroom, that Roger, though he was twenty-seven years old, was still very much under his father's domination. His father did a lot of talking, and though I could not hear what he said I could see that he was talking very forcefully. He was a big man, and the woman I took to be his wife stood beside him and listened respectfully as he spoke. Ben, the boy's uncle, was in the group, and he got in a word or two also. Like the rest, he was a big man.

I still could not identify any of the Gibsons in the courtroom. Neither could Bill Mullen. Ruth was taken by Chloe Adams, the sheriff's office girl and deputy, and led back to the jail immediately when court was recessed. I watched the girl to see if she acknowledged anyone in the room, but she didn't. She said something to Chloe and accompanied her out of the room without looking around.

"Are any of the Gibsons around?" I asked Henry Kemp.

"I don't know any of that family," he said.

"I'm going to ask Bob Day about them when I get a chance," Bill Mullen said.

George Ballentine came wandering back into the courtroom then and, after stopping momentarily to say something to Joe Baumgardner, came over to us.

"We were just talking about the Gibson girl, Sheriff," Bill said to George. "About her family, that is. Have you seen anything of them around?"

"They won't be around for the trial," the sheriff said. "Her father didn't think he could get off work, and her mother has the other kids to look after."

"What kind of folks are they?" I asked.

"They aren't a bad sort of people," he said. "They come from Pomeroy or somewhere around there, I think. Don't amount to much, of course. He works for old John McGillicuddy—you know who I mean, John Martingale's his real name—down there along the river. Just a hand, a pot-walloper. They've got five or six kids. Ruth's the oldest."

"Do they come to see her?" Judge Kemp asked.

"Oh, sure, every week. They can't hardly come in on Friday, the regular visiting day, so I let them see her on Sunday afternoon. Her mother takes her dirty clothes and brings back her clean ones every week, and they generally bring her something to eat—you know, candy and stuff like that."

"How long have they lived around here?" I asked.

"Oh, five or six years, I guess. He come here looking for work and got that job with John. They rented that run-down old place out there."

"Do you think she really did it?" asked Bill Mullen.

"Oh, hell yes, she did," said George. "Sure they did. There's no question in my mind about it. You sort of feel sorry for them, though."

"Want to make a bet on that jury?" Bill asked facetiously. "I'll bet you they vote an acquittal."

"I'll bet they don't," said George, and just then Joe Baumgardner beckoned to him, and he went off to talk to the prosecutor.

Bill rose then. He bid Henry and me good afternoon and left the two of us alone.

Henry and I went to my office and sat down in the comfortable chairs. I gave him a cigar and lit one myself.

"Do you suppose either one of them is a fit subject for probation?" he asked me after a while, breaking into our innocuous conversation about the day.

"Not if they're convicted of armed robbery," I said. "Never in all my days did I put an armed robber on probation. Anyway, you're premature. Worry about that when and if you come to it."

"If they had pleaded guilty I'd have been in a pickle," said Henry. "You don't feel as if you can let a person go scot-free

108

when they've committed a crime like that, and yet you don't want to send them up for ten to twenty-five. I think a judge ought to have more discretion about sentencing than he's got in Ohio."

"Oh, I don't know, Henry," I said. "I've known a few judges, and I'm afraid I wouldn't want to trust too many of them to be entirely dispassionate in their sentencing. Too many of them would have a pet crime that would always get the maximum sentence. It's hard to be calm about crime, you know."

"Well, I suppose so," he agreed.

Then I told him about some of my peeves. Maybe I had told him before. I never could guarantee, even when I was younger, that I would not tell a person the same story more than once, so how can I be expected to do better now? Anyway I told him how angered I have often been when as a judge I have had to administer laws which reflect a legislature's act of irrational hatred. Under the law of Ohio, for example, a judge does not have the discretion to grant probation to persons convicted of certain designated crimes; he must sentence them to terms of imprisonment; he has no power to do anything else once they have been convicted or have pleaded guilty. Among the crimes in this category are murder, arson, burglary of an inhabited dwelling, rape, and administering poison—all crimes of violence which logically belong in this category if there must be such a category. But also included are incest and sodomy! Incest, for God's sake! If a brother and sister indulge in sexual intercourse, or an uncle and niece, they must be sentenced to imprisonment for one to ten years, and the judge has no discretion to place them on probation. Even if they are married to each other! The legislature undoubtedly intended to punish severely the father who forces his daughter to submit to him, but why in the name of God could it not have said so? Relations between an uncle and niece may be socially undesirable and perhaps should be punished to prevent them, but why must this relationship be placed in a category of crimes which compels a court to impose a severe sentence on the offenders? Sodomy is another such crime, even if it occurs between consenting adults. My personal attitude toward sodomy between consenting adults is that it reflects appalling taste. The very thought of the act turns my stomach, and probably it is socially useful to prohibit it and punish violators; but, again, is it a crime which belongs in the same category with murder, arson, and rape? You see, the legislature wallowed in righteousness and committed to the books a statute which has been the source of countless injustices.

Righteousness is a vicious passion. Did you know, I said to Henry Kemp, that the legislature has provided extraordinary police powers to deal with gambling and the distribution of pornography, when extraordinary powers are not available to deal with murder? Of course Henry knew, and he agreed with me about such legislation. What is more, Ohio is fairly liberal about these matters. Other states are much worse. When legislatures act from righteousness, their laws have no limits. Only the constitutions provide us with a degree of protection, but even they are imperiled. Yes, righteousness is a vicious passion, and as an old judge with a high regard for justice, I fear it above all other popular emotions.

Henry and I sat and talked until nearly five o'clock. Both of us appreciate the opportunity to sit together and talk of things common to our experience. I love to pontificate, and Henry is willing to listen. He seems to think he learns something from my experience with his job. He likes to talk about the problems he faces, and I am happy to keep up with what occurs in court, even if I cannot help him. I love to pull down from the walls my beloved volumes of court reports, the accumulated wisdom and foolishness of the courts of Ohio, and lecture on the fine points of the cases that came before me. I knew most of the judges whose opinions are contained in the volumes which cover my years. There was old Chief Justice Carrington T. Marshall, white-bearded old curmudgeon, a most uncivil man. I was glad when young Carl Weygandt became Chief Justice and grew old in the office. I knew Judge Hart and respected him, and the Matthiases, father and son, and Jim Stewart whose son Potter Stewart is a Justice of the Supreme Court of the United States, and Charley Zimmerman. I knew them all. I had ambitions once to join their exalted ranks on the Supreme Court in Columbus, but very few others shared my enthusiasm for the idea, so I stayed here.

Maybe I would not have been happy as an appellate judge anyway, because the work is deadly dry and impersonal. I like to see the people to whom I am dispensing law and justice, like to see them before me in my courtroom and see how they like it. Often I knew I had made a better decision because I had seen them.

When it was almost five o'clock my housekeeper, Mary Gillian, came downtown to drive me home.

I live in a house that belonged to my son, Bill Junior. He and I lived together as two old widowers, and we decided that his small house was better for us than my old one, so I sold mine and moved in with him. He died two years ago at the age of sixty-six. I have another son and two daughters and more grandchildren than I can keep track of, and three or four great-grandchildren for each grandchild. It is a terrible clan of people, and they come around to see me all the time. Aside from my own children, this clan is not really comprised of friends of mine, you know. They come because they respect me and think it is their duty, I suppose. Some of them are nice. I cannot recommend the office of patriarch, however, and I try not to practice at it any more than I have to, to satisfy the demands of courtesy. Mary Gillian suits me. She is thirty-five or so, a colored girl I granted a divorce to some years ago. My house does not require much cleaning, and I do not require much cooking because I eat out so often, so her job is not too difficult. She is very responsible. I can trust her. She prepared a good dinner as she always does, and afterward she took me back downtown to the Masonic Temple because it was lodge night.

I have been a Mason since I was old enough to be one, and I went through the chairs and was master of our lodge. At ninety-two years of age, it is inevitable that I should be the oldest living past master, and it is treated as though it were an accomplishment. Like all Masonic lodges, ours is on the second floor of the building; a pharmacy occupies the first. When I am too old to climb the stairs I will have to quit the lodge, and I will lose one of the pleasures of my life. I could not tell you why I go. I have, of course, seen the ritual thousands of times, performed correctly and otherwise, and still I like to sit in a comfortable chair and see the boys go through it. Anyone who says the meetings are not dull is lying or too stupid to realize that they are, and yet they have a flavor, a certain appeal, that brings you back again and again, once you have learned to appreciate it. It is an acquired taste, like ripe olives and Scotch whisky, and like those it has a strong attraction once the taste is learned. Maybe the attraction is in the realization that you are watching a ritual that has been essentially the same since—who knows when? One feels a kinship broad and horizontal with the thousands and thousands of Masons today, and also vertical with the other thousands who have performed this ritual for centuries and presumably will do it for centuries more. Some of it is foolish and childish, and you can pick at it, but the whole is beautiful and inspiring and enduring, and it is worth the vast accumulation of time I have spent in lodge.

They call me Bill at the Masonic Temple, which I like. I don't want to be so damned old that no one dares call me by my first name any more. I went directly to the lodge room and did not stop by the social rooms. I put on my white apron and took my seat on the sideline. We had our meeting, about which I can say nothing because that, of course, is secret; and then we went into the dining room where the stewards served pie and ice cream and coffee.

The talk around the table was about the trial. The more so because they knew I had been there and they wanted to hear what I might say about it.

The older hands around the lodge led the conversation, at least at first. This was a privilege that went with age.

"Well, things are in a pretty state when a man can't run a business right down in the middle of a town without having to worry about it being robbed in broad daylight," said an old doctor friend of mine.

"Well, what are you going to do, what are you going to do?" asked another old man, a retired carpenter.

That kind of question does not seem to call for an answer, so the doctor said, "You can't tell me things like that happened years ago."

"Well, I will tell you so," said a third old man, owner of a magazine and greeting-card shop. "I can remember stores being robbed two or three times. Shoot, we had the Holt case, just to mention one. Then there was the time the bank . . ."

"Well, the banks have never been robbed, thank God," said the doctor. "What you're talking about there is an embezzlement."

"Well, they got the money, didn't they? It amounts to the same thing."

"No, it doesn't. There's a difference between sneak theft on the one hand, and on the other hand using a gun and holding somebody up. Isn't that so, Bill?" the doctor said to me.

I replied that the law recognized a difference.

Then the doctor said that times had changed since he was a boy, just as I knew he would sooner or later. "People act differently now," he insisted. There is, of course, no point in arguing about that. I can remember my father saying that I was growing up in a sinful age and was part of a sinful generation. So can any son of any articulate parent throughout the ages of history. When have the old not said this about the young? But I like one reply I heard when an old woman was saying how they didn't do this and that when she was a girl, and another old woman, her contemporary, spoke up and said that if she didn't then she'd missed a lot of fun, for the other young people of the day were doing it.

One of the younger members of the lodge said he was fairly well acquainted with both Roger Louis and Ruth Gibson. The others pressed him to talk, and he said he did not like Louis because Louis was a bully and a drunk, but he said he liked Ruth Gibson and was sorry to have seen her associate with Louis. He said Ruth would not be in trouble except for her association with Louis. Paul Russell's explanation had been different, I said. The young man said he would not believe a word from Paul Russell about anything. Several others defended Russell, and one of them said that the first young man's estimate was colored by his own affection for Ruth Gibson.

"Well," he said in reply, "she's just a little country girl that came into town, got a job and doesn't know any better than to let people take advantage of her."

"She was laying her tail down for anybody who wanted it, wasn't she?" said one of the others.

"No," insisted the first. "She was nuts for Doc Russell, fell for

113

his line, and she probably did let him have what he wanted. But then he went around and bragged about it, just the way he always does, and that gave her a bad reputation."

I said I had observed that she and Louis did not seem to care much for each other any more, since they did not even speak in the courtroom.

"Well, I can tell you why," said a man who had not spoken until then. "The Louises all think she got Roger into trouble. They believe Doc Russell, except they think Doc is mistaken in his identification. They think Doc pointed to the first guy the sheriff picked up because he looked something like the guy who did it, and besides, he was with her. They're all madder than hell at her. Then she's mad at Roger because she thinks he could have put up her bond and got her out of jail too. Of course, he couldn't. He couldn't even put up his own. His folks did it, put some land up for it. But she thinks he could have taken care of her bond too. She thinks he has left her high and dry."

"How do you know?" someone asked.

"One of the fellows at work was telling it. He knows the Louises pretty well. Besides, old Sally Hodges was in jail for drunk and disorderly twice since Ruth Gibson's been there, and she says that Ruth told her all about it."

"Did she tell Sally she did it?"

"No, she told Sally she didn't do it. She told Sally that Doc Russell was trying to frame her."

"Why?"

"She didn't say why."

"Well, there's one thing I'd like to know," said the doctor. "If they weren't guilty, then why'd they run like mad at the first sight of the sheriff?"

"Yeah," said the carpenter. "Those two lawyers are going to have some time trying to explain that."

"Well," said the doctor, "I've known Paul Russell for some years, and I think he's a pretty solid young man. You put that together with their running like that, and you put the kind of characters that the two of them are in with it, and it spells guilty if I know how to spell."

"No, sir," said the young man who liked Ruth Gibson. "I

114

wouldn't believe Doc Russell, and that's all the evidence they've got against them."

The doctor opened his mouth to argue, but the carpenter interrupted and said, "Well, you can't tell until you hear the rest of it. There's no use arguing about it. You can't tell anything until you hear what they're going to say tomorrow."

I agreed, and having said so, I went to call Mary to come for me.

VI

IT RAINED the next day, and wet umbrellas sat in the corners of the room, under the seats, in the jury box. Wet raincoats spread over chairs, and Quentin, ever the guardian of the county's property, scurried about moving them and shaking them and admonishing their owners. The two lovers on the jury, Walter Taylor and Linda Tubman, came in together; someone told me they had been out on a date the night before. William Cleveland, the farmer, carried in some red mud on his shoes and deposited it in the jury box. Roger Louis came in, wearing precisely the same clothes he had worn the first day. Ruth Gibson had changed, however. She was still wearing the gray skirt and the light blue blouse, but she had left behind the gray coat with the padding in the shoulders, the other half of her suit. Her attorney had advised this change. He didn't want her to look too bad.

The principal characters found their places, and the trial resumed at nine-thirteen.

Joe Baumgardner called Michael Thomas Bradstreet as his first witness on the second day of the trial. Mike came in and took his seat. He is a nice-looking young man, a big, sun-tanned fellow who likes being a deputy sheriff. He tips his hat forward on his head, as he supposes a deputy should. Mike was a deputy before George was elected sheriff, and helped George over many of the rough spots during the first few months of George's tenure. Some say Mike would have liked to run for the office himself, but I know he acknowledges the shortcoming which would deny him the position; he has no political savvy whatever, and could never win an election. He does his job efficiently and without much comment.

"State your full name, please."

"Michael Thomas Bradstreet."

"And your address."

"Rural Route 2, Alexandria."

"And where are you employed?"

"I am deputy sheriff of Marshall County."

"I direct your attention to May 20, 1961, and ask you if you were in the sheriff's office when a call reported a robbery at DeWitt's Jewelry Store?"

"I was in the office when that call came in."

"What time was that?"

"Nine-thirty, quarter of ten."

"As a consequence of that call did you go out to look for a suspect?"

"Yes, I did."

"Did you go alone?"

"No, I went with the sheriff."

"Where did you go?"

"Well, first we had to serve a summons or two. Then we went to the Gibson place."

"By the Gibson place do you mean the home of Joel and Mary Gibson?"

"Yes, sir, on County Road Five."

"Why did you go there?"

"Well, the call that came in said Ruth Gibson had been seen sitting in the getaway car, so we figured we would go out there and see if her folks knew where she was or where we could find her."

"Who did you talk to at the Gibson place?"

"To her father and mother."

"Joel and Mary Gibson?"

"Yes, sir."

"What did they tell you?"

"Nothin' much. We asked them about the boys their daughter ran around with, and they gave us a couple of names."

"After talking with the Gibsons what did you do?"

"Well, we sat in the car and talked about it some. One of the names they gave us was Roger Louis, and I remembered I had arrested him once—"

"Objection," said Bob Day.

"Yes," said the judge to the witness. "Never mind about any arrests other than in this case." He turned to the prosecutor. "Go on," Henry said.

Joe Baumgardner paused before he asked the witness to continue. From the beginning of Bradstreet's testimony, it had been obvious what Joe would do. The deputy could not add anything to George Ballentine's testimony, and Baumgardner knew it as well as everybody else in the courtroom. He was merely leading him through the same questions, expecting the same answers, and reinforcing the sheriff's report for the jury. The better Joe could stack his case, the better his chances for conviction. He looked at the witness and asked him to go on.

Mike nodded. "Well, I thought I could remember what Roger Louis looked like. I remembered he was a sort of dark fellow, something like they had told us to look for. So we figured we might as well go and see if we could find where he was. We happened to be pretty close to Ben Louis's place, so we went there and asked about this Roger. They told us he was Jack Louis's boy, so we went to see Jack. Jack told us his boy had a car like the one we were looking for, so we figured we better keep on looking for Roger Louis. The sheriff, he remembered the old house on Shambles Ridge that belongs to another one of the Louises—Sherm, I guess it is, and we decided to go and take a look there. I'd been up there lots of times to roust out people that was—shacking up." Mike shrugged his shoulders and grinned, as if to ask what other phrase anyone wanted to suggest. "Anyway, we went up there."

"What happened when you got there?"

"When we started walking up toward the house, a couple went running out the back door."

"Well, let's go back a little bit. Did you find a car there?"

"Yes, there was a light green 1950 Chevrolet there that we later identified as belonging to Roger Louis."

"Then as you approached the house—"

"Roger Louis and Ruth Gibson ran out the back door."

"Did you run after them?"

"Yes, we ran up the hill after them. We hollered at them to stop, but they didn't, and the sheriff, he fired a shot in the air. But they kept on going just the same."

"Did you catch them?"

"Well, we caught her. We could see them scrambling up the hill ahead of us, and we seen her drop down and sort of crawl behind this log and into this clump of brush. So we just ran right up to her and caught her easy. But the fellow, he had started down the other side of the hill and had been out of our sight for a minute or so, and when we got to the top we couldn't see him anywheres."

"Did you keep on running?"

"No, we stopped. The sheriff stopped to take care of the girl. I run on ahead a little ways to look for the fellow, but I had to stop and look around. We looked all around for a while, figuring he'd hid somewhere like she tried to do, but we didn't get anywhere that way. While we were looking he was working his way on down the hill, out of our sight because of the trees, and he got too far away from us for us to chase him any more. So we give it up."

"Then did you go back to Ruth Gibson?"

"Yes. For a minute." Mike stopped to laugh. "The sheriff, he'd put his handcuffs on her legs because there wasn't anything solid right there to attach her to, and he had to keep her from getting away again while we went after the other one. She'd hopped around some, but she couldn't get far."

119

"Do you mean she had tried to escape?"

"Objection," said Bob Day.

"Well, put it this way then," said Baumgardner. "Had she moved away from the place where you caught her?"

"A little, just a little," replied the witness. "She wasn't going to go far that way."

"All right. Then what happened?"

"Well, I went back down to our car to call in, and the sheriff took the girl in the house."

"After you made your radio call, did you come back to the house?"

"Yes, sir."

"What did you do there?"

"We searched the place but didn't find nothing."

"Did Ruth Gibson talk to you while you were in the house?"

"Yes, she did."

"Tell us about that."

"Well, we searched the house. The sheriff had handcuffed her to a big iron bed in the bedroom, and I went in there—"

"Where was the sheriff at this point?"

"Down in the basement, I think."

"Go on then."

"Well, I went in the bedroom, and she was sitting on the bed and crying a little, and she says to me, 'Why don't you let me go? Why don't you let me go?' a couple times. I said, 'Not on your life, after all the trouble we went to to catch you.' She said, 'You know me, Mike. Why don't you let me go?'"

"You knew her before?" Baumgardner interrupted.

"She'd waited on me over there at the restaurant. Anyway, I told her she was being held on a serious charge, and I said she might as well cooperate with us. She said she'd give me all kinds of cooperation if I'd let her go."

"Was that all she said?"

"That's all she said then. I went out of the room and didn't talk to her any more right then."

"Did she talk to you in the car on your way back to town?"

"Yes."

"Tell us about that."

"Well, what she said was, she asked us two or three times how long her sentence would be, and finally the sheriff told her ten years, and then she started to cry pretty hard."

"Did she ask you any other questions?"

"No, not that I remember."

"Did she ask how you knew where to look for the two of them?"

"I don't remember her asking that, no."

"When you reached town, what did you do?"

"Well, we brought her in and had her put in jail, and then we went back out to get the fellow, but another car had picked him up too."

"Is the Ruth Gibson we have been talking about present in the courtroom?"

"Yes, that's her sitting right over there."

"Let the record show," said the prosecuting attorney, "that the witness has identified the defendant Ruth Gibson."

Roger Louis leaned toward MacInroth and whispered to him. Ruth Gibson did not move but continually looked at the witness. Bob Day said something to her occasionally, and she would nod, but she did not look his way. She was so impassive that the first impression her appearance created—that of being a pitiful creature caught in a trap—was being gradually replaced in my mind, and I am sure in the minds of the jurors too, by an image of a woman drawing strength from desperation, and with more maturity than appearance alone suggested. Louis was keeping first impression intact. He remained nervous and morose, and his comments to MacInroth were frequent. His manner suggested that he was uncomfortable, impatient, and eager to conclude the trial, however it came out. Also, he turned frequently and looked to his father and uncle in the back. They nodded or shook their heads or winked, as the occasion seemed to demand, but one could not guess that they were giving Roger Louis any reassurance.

"Were you present," asked the prosecuting attorney of the deputy, "when Paul Russell was brought to the courthouse to identify the suspect who had been picked up by the other deputies?"

"Yes."

"Describe that."

"Well, Bob and Jim—"

"By Bob and Jim you mean deputies Robert Delaney and James Handschumacher?"

"That's right. They had picked up Roger Louis. And they brought him in, and when the sheriff and I got back they had him in jail. The chief of police came in, and he went and got Doc Russell from the store. We got some others and lined them up with Roger Louis, and Russell identified Roger Louis as the man who had robbed him."

"Is the man identified by Paul Russell present in the courtroom?"

"Yes, that's him there."

Roger Louis shook his head vigorously.

"Is that the same man you saw run out of the house on Shambles Ridge and whom you pursued up the hill?"

"Yes, he's the one."

"Thank you. That's all," said Joe Baumgardner. He was pleased. Mike Bradstreet had effectively reinforced the sheriff's testimony, and George Ballentine's testimony would be all the more effective for it.

Bob Day cross-examined. I was not the only one interested in Bob's courtroom performance. Up till now he had not performed extensively, though I could see he was carrying his share of the load. One could not yet tell how good a trial lawyer he would be, but we could watch his manner and guess what he was thinking and feeling. Whereas MacInroth frequently scribbled notes, Day usually sat with his chair pushed back from the table and his legs crossed. He was better dressed than the other two lawyers—had better taste in clothes; and he looked neat and prosperous, although of course of these lawyers his practice was by far the smallest. His wife and father were in the courtroom most of the time, and I think I observed correctly that Day never looked at them until the court recessed. He looked calm, but I think he was working hard at seeming so. I noticed that he held something in his hands all the time, usually a pencil, and that whatever he held in his fingers he wiggled constantly. When I say he did not take many notes I do not mean to say he didn't have any. He was using MacInroth's. MacInroth is an inveterate note-taker. He scribbled all through the trial, and probably Day thought that one complete set of notes was enough. MacInroth pushed his notes over to him, Day nodded his thanks politely, and he looked at the yellow papers for a moment before beginning.

"You testified that when Paul Russell was confronted with a line of men he pointed out Roger Louis and identified him as the man who robbed him, isn't that right?"

"Yes, sir."

"What, if anything, did Roger Louis say at that point?"

"Well, he was pretty mad, and he said he'd never seen Russell before and Russell was crazy."

"In other words, he denied that Russell had correctly identified him."

"Yes, that's right. He denied it."

"Has the sheriff discussed with you my cross-examination of him on the subject of that lineup?"

"No, sir."

"Is it your testimony that the sheriff did not tell you that I criticized his conduct of the identification because none of the other men with whom Russell was confronted was the sort of man Russell had described?"

"Oh," said the deputy quickly, "yes, he told me about that."

"Do you agree then that none of the other men in the lineup looked like the one Russell had described as the man who robbed him?"

"Well, none of the other men looked anything like Roger Louis."

Bob Day stood up but stayed behind his table. "All right, Mike," he said, "we can go about it the long way if you want to take the time. What kind of man did Russell say robbed him?"

"A medium-height man, dark-complected, with dark hair."

"And you had been given that description by the police before you went out to look for anyone?"

"Yes."

"How many men did you have in the lineup that had dark complexions and dark hair and were of medium height?"

"Just one."

"And which one was that?"

"Roger Louis."

Mike Bradstreet did not understand Day's objection to the lineup. Neither, I think, did the sheriff entirely, though he showed signs of comprehension that Bradstreet did not. Some of the jurors seemed to understand. Cleveland, the hill farmer, and Schwallie, the shoe-store manager, smiled knowingly at Day while he was making this point, as they had from time to time at each of the attorneys. But jurors are deceptive. You never know what they are thinking. I prefer a quiet, unresponsive juror who never shows any sign either of emotion or of comprehension—one like Joe Paccinelli, juror number two.

"In other words, Russell could not have identified anyone else in the lineup?"

"No. No one else," the witness said readily. Of course, I knew that for Mike this only proved the validity of the identification.

"So we can never know, can we, what Paul Russell would have done if he had been confronted with a group of dark men of medium height?"

"Objection," interceded the prosecuting attorney. "I think he has made his point and the question just argues it."

Judge Henry Kemp made a quick gesture with his hand. He pressed it to his forehead and brushed back his hair, all very abruptly, and then he drew his hand down the side of his cheek more slowly. "Yes," he said, "I think you've made your point, counselor. Go on to something else."

Bob Day pulled his chair out and sat down. He drew his lower lip in between his teeth and looked to the yellow legal pad before him. "Did you search the house on Shambles Ridge?" he asked quietly.

"Yes."

"Looking for what?"

"The missing jewelry. Money. A gun."

"And a blue jacket?"

"No, I wasn't looking for a jacket."

"Did you search the car?"

"Yes."

"And the persons of the defendants?"

"No. I wasn't there when Louis was arrested, and we didn't search the girl."

"Well, do you think she was carrying anything much on her person when she ran out of the house?"

"No."

"What was she wearing?"

"A white shirt and a pair of shorts."

"Could she have concealed anything much in those?"

"No, she didn't conceal much of anything in those clothes," said the deputy impishly. Everyone in the courtroom laughed, even the judge, who tried not to.

Bob Day laughed too, and he waited a moment before asking, "Did you find, with all this searching, either the gun used in the robbery, or the money, or the jewelry?"

"No."

"Never found anything?"

"No, never did."

"When you searched the house did you find some clothing belonging to the defendants?"

"Yes."

"Specifically, did you find her underclothing?"

"Yes, there was a brassière and a pair of panties she said was hers."

"During the time between her capture and the time you turned Ruth Gibson over to Chloe Adams to be put in jail, did you ever use the words 'robbery' or 'armed robbery' to her?"

"No, I didn't."

"Did you hear the sheriff use either of those terms to her?"

"No."

"Did she say anything to you during that time about a robbery?"

"No."

"Did any of the three of you, in your hearing, say anything about DeWitt's store?"

"No."

"When you were searching the house, did you tell her what you were looking for, or did you hear the sheriff tell her?"

"Not that I recall."

"Did she give you any indication that she knew she was being arrested for the robbery of Dewitt's store?"

The witness did not answer. He blinked several times and then he looked down at the floor.

"Did she?" Bob Day asked after a moment.

"Well, I don't remember just anything she said that was . . . I don't remember she said anything exactly that was about the robbery, not exactly."

"Your answer is no, then?"

"Well . . . yes, I guess so."

"When was the first time the words 'robbery' or 'armed robbery' were used to her?"

"Well, offhand I couldn't say."

"But not before you got her to the courthouse. You're sure of that?"

"Yes."

"Did you hear the sheriff say to Chloe Adams that here was the girl wanted for robbery, or words to that effect?"

"Yes, I heard him say that, something like that."

"Could that have been the first time Ruth Gibson heard the words, heard the charge against her stated?"

"I suppose maybe that was the first time anyone said to her exactly what the charge was. We supposed she knew."

"What was her reaction when she heard that?"

"She started to cry."

"Hysterically?"

"Pretty loud."

"All right. Did she ever say to you she was not Ruth Gibson?"

"No."

"Did you hear her say that to the sheriff?"

"No."

"All right. That's all."

Joe Baumgardner stood up. "Did Ruth Gibson say anything to you that suggested she thought she was charged with any crime other than armed robbery?"

"No."

"When, in the sheriff's office, she heard the sheriff say she was charged with armed robbery, did she say she was not guilty of it?"

"No, she just started to cry."

"Without denying the charge?"

"Yes."

"Thank you. That's all," said Joe Baumgardner. He sat down and consulted his notes while Bradstreet walked toward the door. Then he looked up to Quentin and said, "Call James Handschumacher."

Quentin followed Bradstreet out into the corridor and called out the name. In a moment Handschumacher came in and took his place in the witness box.

"State your full name, please."

"James Handschumacher."

"Your address."

"I live in the apartment with the sheriff and his wife."

"You mean the county apartment in the jail building?"

"Yes, I live in the apartment with the sheriff and his wife."

"And you are a deputy?"

"Yes, I've been a deputy sheriff fourteen years."

He has, too. He is a little man, about forty-five years old, with only a fringe of graying hair on the perimeter of his bald head. During his first year as a deputy, he marched into a roadhouse to arrest a drunk who was shooting out the lights with a pistol. A bullet shattered the bone in his hip, and now he walks with a distressing limp. Everyone knows he suffers some pain which he will not admit. He is not a very competent deputy, but of course he will always keep his job. He is married, but his wife does not live with him, and as he said, he lives in the sheriff's apartment and acts as jailer. He would rather patrol in a car, but he cannot drive because of his leg, so he goes out only when another man needs his help. He is, of course, the son of another of our German families, one of the few German families which never owned land, a family rather of artisans—carpenters, printers, and bakers. The Handschumacher and Baumgardner families are dissimilar. The Baumgardners looked down on the Handschumachers. The Handschumachers were Catholics at first, but now only one family of them is. When the Baumgardners used to have their parties at the big white farmhouse, they did not invite the Handschumachers, and the Handschumachers and the other German Catholic families would meet in a beer garden and have a party of their own with lots of beer and much sneering at the high and mighty Baumgardners. I can remember those people too, from the turn of the century; they were clannish, they clung to their native language and they devoted themselves fiercely to their religion, though it was not an esteemed religion in this community at that time. They hoarded their money and built the biggest church in town, with a high steeple that stands above the trees and proclaims the faith and pride of the German Catholics to the Protestants below. The Germans assimilated; few of them remain with the Church now. The church they built belongs now to the Irish and Italians and to the American Catholics, who are now, in the century of brotherhood, religionists of a faith as well thought of here as any other, and they no longer have to be clannish.

"I direct your attention," said Joe Baumgardner, "to the twentieth day of May of this year and ask you if you were in the sheriff's office when a call came in reporting a robbery at De-Witt's Jewelry Store."

"No, I wasn't in the office right when that call come in," Handschumacher replied in a high-pitched nervous voice. "I was back in the jail seeing to it that some cleaning got done back there. Prisoners'd never clean up if you didn't watch them and make them do it."

"But you heard about that call?"

"I come out to the office, and the sheriff and Mike had gone out looking for the suspects. Chloe told me where they had gone and why. That was when I first heard about the whole business."

"Did you, later, go out to look for one of the suspects?"

"We got a radio call that the sheriff and Mike had caught the girl, and the fellow had run into the woods. We got in a car and went out there in that neighborhood to see if we couldn't find the one that run off."

"Who else went with you in the car?"

"It was Bob Delaney that went with me. He came in and was

in the office when that radio call went in, and I said to him, 'Let's you and me go on that call,' and we went."

"Where did you go?"

"Out toward Shambles Ridge. There's a lot of different roads in that area, county roads and township roads and private roads too. We was going to drive up and down them and see if we could find this fellow Roger Louis. There was another car answered that call, and we called him on the radio and sort of divided up roads between us, and we took some roads to look on, and he took the others."

Handschumacher talks jerkily, stopping every sentence or so to swallow his saliva, and when he swallows he bobs his head up and down a little. He leaned forward in his chair and stared intently at the prosecutor, occasionally breaking his stare to turn and look at the jury. He gestures when he talks, and these movements are quick and jerky too. Whenever he speaks of anything serious, Handschumacher is intent and humorless. On the witness stand he was all the more intent and humorless.

"Did you take a suspect into custody?"

"Yes. Yes, we caught the fellow. We come up on him walking out there on what they call Pine Tree Road. He was just walking along, and we drove up beside him and caught him easy. We asked him if he was Roger Louis, and he looked at us kind of funny for a minute and then said he was. We told him he was under arrest for the robbery of DeWitt's store. He said we was crazy because he'd never been in DeWitt's store in his life. He was kind of mad, so we got out and put handcuffs on him and made him get in the car."

"And then did you take him back to town?"

"Yes."

"Did he talk to you on the way back?"

"Some. Not very much. He wasn't very talkative."

"Did he say anything about Ruth Gibson?"

"Once he said if it wasn't for that damned girl he wouldn't be in any trouble. I suppose he meant—"

"Objection," snapped Bob Day. "What he thinks the defendant meant is not evidence."

"Yes," said the judge. "Just tell what you are asked."

"I just figured it was what he meant," protested Handschumacher in manifest embarrassment.

"Well, what you figure he meant is not evidence in the case," said the judge definitely. "Just tell us what you saw or heard, as you are asked, and don't tell us what you thought of what you saw or heard."

Handschumacher flushed and said, "All right, your Honor."

"Did he say anything about Paul Russell?"

"Yes, he said he should have shot him."

"He's a goddamn liar!" Louis said to MacInroth in a harsh whisper heard all over the room.

Handschumacher heard it, and looked hard at Louis. A buzz and murmur traveled over the courtroom. Everyone recognized a telling point.

Baumgardner, however, had not finished making his point. "Had either you or Delaney mentioned the name Paul Russell, or Doc Russell, to Roger Louis?"

"No, neither one of us had said anything to him about who had been in the store when it was robbed."

"And what were his specific words about Paul Russell?"

"He said, 'I should have shot that goddamned Russell.' "

Again there was a disturbance in the courtroom. Louis turned toward his father in the back of the room and shook his head. MacInroth and Day conferred in whispers, and when they had finished, Ruth Gibson sought Day's ear and said something to him. On the witness stand, Handschumacher showed that he understood the importance of what he had said. His face was red and the light caught beads of perspiration on his forehead. The jury understood it too. The slouching ones sat up, and all of them were observing closely the reactions of the principals.

"Did he say anything else?"

"Only that we were crazy to arrest him, that he didn't have anything to do with it, and that he wanted to see a lawyer as soon as he got to town."

"What did you do with him when you got him to town?"

"We put him right in a cell until the sheriff could get back to talk to him."

"Is the man you arrested on Pine Tree Road in the courtroom?"

Handschumacher tipped his head and looked quizzically at Baumgardner. "Sure," he said, "that's him right there," in a voice that suggested he thought the prosecuting attorney must have lost his reason. The people in the courtroom laughed, and Handschumacher flushed again.

Baumgardner turned to the two defense lawyers and said, "You may cross-examine."

MacInroth and Day sat and talked for a moment. It was plain they had been surprised. Handschumacher had made two points, not just one: first, that Louis acknowledged having committed the crime by his comment about Russell; and second, that Louis himself volunteered the name of Russell. It implied that young Louis knew who had been robbed, a fact only the robber could have known. MacInroth and Day had anticipated everything so far put in evidence by the prosecution, but they had not anticipated this. It was a blow. It had impressed the jury. And, of course, they did not know how to counter it. The more they conferred, the more they impressed the importance of the point on the minds of the jury, so they broke it off as quickly as they could, and MacInroth rose to cross-examine.

MacInroth was in an unfortunate position. He had nothing to cross-examine about. The first rule of cross-examination is not to try it unless you can accomplish something by it. You must come into cross-examination prepared to examine. You may seek further information from the witness. You may point out a discrepancy in his story. You may lay the groundwork to discredit him with a future witness. You may attack the credibility of the witness by pointing up defects in his character. But you must pursue one of these lines. It is a mistake simply to lead the witness through his story again unless you know there is an error in it. If you do, the jury only hears the witness tell his tale twice instead of once. If you unsuccessfully attack his credibility, you may alienate the jury, who will sympathize with the poor witness undergoing unfriendly cross-examination. I have heard lawyers press a witness, saying, "Are you sure about that?" and the witness would say, "Sure, I'm sure." The jury would take note that the witness *was* sure, and the lawyer lost a point. Courtroom dramas make too much of cross-examination. To authors and playwrights it is drama, the clash of wits and personalities, and it makes dazzling fiction. That is very well for fiction. It is disastrous for the trial lawyer if he approaches cross-examination with some such idea in *his* mind. The high point of every television trial comes when the witness breaks down on cross-examination and tearfully admits *he* killed the victim and would again if he could. In my years in the courtroom no witness ever confessed from the stand. I have never even seen a criminal give up his defense and admit his guilt, even if he later admitted it after conviction. It simply does not happen.

Now MacInroth was in a pickle. He had nothing to go on, and yet if he sat down without questioning Handschumacher, he would tacitly and dramatically be admitting that Handschumacher was telling the truth.

"You don't much like Roger Louis, do you?" MacInroth asked Handschumacher casually, looking down at his notes as he asked it.

Handschumacher shrugged. "I got nothing against him."

"Were you acquainted with him before you arrested him?"

"I'd seen him around."

"Where?"

"Places. Bars."

"Ever talk to him?"

"No."

MacInroth was fishing. He was not making a point. Yet even so, the cross-examination differed from that between the defense attorneys and the other law officers. Handschumacher was hostile. To the other deputy, to the sheriff, and to the chief of police testimony was only a job, a process in which they were not personally involved. The sheriff and Bradstreet scrupulously tried at least to appear impartial. Handschumacher, however, plainly did not like to be cross-examined. Like many other witnesses I have seen, he took it as a challenge. He did not understand that the lawyer was doing a job he had to do. Handschumacher had told his story. As far as he was concerned, the story was final, and no good could come of answering questions of defense counsel. The way he saw it, the lawyer was trying to prove him a liar, and he was not going to help him do it.

"Have you ever testified against a defendant who was acquitted?" MacInroth asked, playing on the hostility of his witness.

"I don't remember."

"Has everybody you ever arrested gone to jail or prison?"

"I don't suppose so."

"Some of them were innocent, then?"

"They said they were."

"Judges and juries said they were too, didn't they?"

"That's what they said."

"But you never made a mistake, did you?"

"I'll object to that," Baumgardner interrupted the beginning of Handschumacher's answer.

"Yes, I can't see any point in that," said the Judge. "Go on to something else."

At this point I noticed that Ruth Gibson had been whispering for several moments to Bob Day. Bob reached up and touched MacInroth's arm. MacInroth leaned over and listened to Bob for a moment. Then he straightened up and asked another question.

"Tell me, Deputy," he said, "what you think of Ruth here."

Handschumacher hesitated a moment and then said, "I got nothin' against her either."

"You liked her pretty well at one time, didn't you?"

"I don't know," Handschumacher shrugged. "I never knew her very well."

"You asked her for dates more than once, didn't you?"

"No, I never did," asserted Handschumacher.

"Do you deny that you ever asked her for a date?"

"Well, I offered her a drink once or twicet. That's all, just offered her a drink. I didn't proposition her."

"Well, were you to have the drink in the place where she works?"

"No, not there." Handschumacher was reddening again. He was nervous. You could almost hear him thinking. If he denied any flirtation with the girl, they might produce witnesses to testify he had been friendly to her. If he admitted the flirtation, he would look bad. Handschumacher was in a quandary.

"Well, if you were not to have this drink together there, then you had to go somewhere else to have it, hey?" pressed MacInroth.

"I guess so."

"And if you took her somewhere else to have a drink, wouldn't that be what is commonly called a date with her?"

"I don't know what you call it." A certain sign that a witness is uncomfortable and would lie if he thought he could succeed is this retreat into phrases like "I guess" and "I don't know." Of course, it also shows his hostility toward the cross-examiner.

"Well, if you take a girl out for a drink, that's a date, isn't it?"

"Maybe."

"No, it's not maybe." MacInroth was pushing the witness hard. "It's either yes or no. Which is it, Deputy?"

"If I take a girl out for a drink, it's a date, I suppose," said Handschumacher angrily. "But that's not—"

"All right, that's the answer," MacInroth interrupted him, speaking up loudly to cut off the rest of Handschumacher's sentence. It was the most angry moment we had seen so far in the trial. "Now I think you should be able to tell us on a yes or no basis if you asked this girl for a date."

"Now I want to say this—" Handschumacher burst out angrily.

"I don't care what you want to say," MacInroth shouted, arousing the whole courtroom. "I want you to answer the questions you are asked. If the court please, I ask that the witness be directed to answer what he is asked without offering his comments."

Judge Kemp paused for a moment, intending to let the tension subside. "You will have to answer the questions," he told Handschumacher. "You will have to let the lawyers run the trial."

Actually, of course, Handschumacher's conduct had not been unusual, but, without anything else to examine about, MacInroth was glad to play on the hostility of the witness.

"Now the question was," MacInroth said, advancing across the floor to confront Handschumacher, "if you asked Ruth Gibson for a date. Yes or no?"

"I asked her to go out for a drink," said Handschumacher bitterly.

"Then that's yes, isn't it?" insisted MacInroth.

Handschumacher glowered. His face was red and his knuckles white. "Yes," he said finally.

"All right," said MacInroth quietly. "Now did you ask her to go out for a drink with you once, or more than once?"

"A couple times, I suppose."

"Or three?"

"Maybe three."

"Or four?"

"No, no more than three times."

"Okay, so you asked her for a date three times, then. But she didn't accept your invitation, did she?"

"No."

"You didn't like that much, did you?"

"It didn't make much difference to me," said Handschumacher haughtily.

"But, of course, she did accept the invitations of Roger Louis, didn't she?"

"I don't know."

MacInroth leaned against the rail of the jury box. His fishing expedition had turned out better than he had hoped. He was enjoying himself—at least he made it appear so. That was a part of his performance.

"You weren't jealous of Roger Louis, I suppose?"

"No. She wasn't going with him at the time when I asked her." Handschumacher regained his composure in that answer. He had caught the drift of the questioning and had anticipated this question. He gave the answer MacInroth did not want to hear, and now he was glad he had been given the opportunity. Maybe he *could* trade words with this smart-aleck lawyer.

If such were Handschumacher's thoughts, he was wrong. MacInroth had been saving the point he was really pursuing. "Anyway, Deputy, you did ask this girl for a date two or three times. You asked her to go out and have a drink with you. Tell me, Handschumacher, aren't you married?"

Handschumacher's moment of relaxation was over, and he was angry and blushing again. "I don't live with my wife," he said.

"But you *have* a wife, don't you?" asked MacInroth in mock innocence.

135

"Yes, somewhere," said Handschumacher.

"Hmmm," said MacInroth. "Well, we'll spare you the embarrassment of going into your domestic difficulties, though I suspect you have explained them. Let's go on to something else."

Baumgardner rose. "Now, if the court please," he said, "we can't just sit here and let *that* go into the record. I ask that counsel's comment on the state of the witness's domestic difficulties be stricken and the jury be instructed to disregard it. I also think the court might appropriately say a word to counsel regarding propriety."

"I will not be lectured to about courtroom propriety," said MacInroth aggressively.

"Maybe not by the prosecuting attorney, Mr. MacInroth," said the judge authoritatively. "But by the court you will if the court decides you need it. Now, I do think your comment that the witness has explained his domestic difficulty by his testimony goes too far, and I would appreciate it if you take a bit more care with your comments. You can argue the case when the time comes. The jury is instructed to disregard the comment we have mentioned."

Baumgardner sat down. MacInroth went back to his table and picked up his yellow legal pad, though it did not contain a note about Handschumacher's cross-examination, and then he returned to the rail of the jury box. He had been set back by the court, but at least three of the jurors had laughed at his comment and appreciated the humor. To tell a jury to disregard something they have seen or heard rarely works, and MacInroth knew it as well as Joe Baumgardner, Henry Kemp and I.

"Mr. Handschumacher," said MacInroth in a precise, reasoning tone, "you have been rather glad, have you not, to have Ruth Gibson in your jail?"

"No," said Handschumacher simply, shaking his head. He apparently had decided not to let MacInroth anger him again.

"Well, you spend a lot of time back there in the women's jail talking to her, don't you?"

"No," said Handschumacher again.

"Well, don't you spend more time there than you customarily did before she was there?"

"Yes," said Handschumacher agreeably.

"Why?"

"Well, most of the time she's the only person back there. I suppose she must be lonesome, and it seemed like a nice thing to do to go back and talk to her sometimes."

There is a time to cross-examine and a time to stop, and MacInroth recognized the time to stop. He had done much better than he could have expected, and to go on now would only obscure the one or two points he had managed to make. He went over to Bob Day and asked him if he had anything else to ask, and when Bob said no, he terminated the cross-examination.

Baumgardner decided not to make any redirect examination. Laying emphasis on what had been said would have been pointless.

Handschumacher was dismissed. I might add that he does not speak to MacInroth to this day.

The prosecutor called Robert Delaney, the other deputy of the pair who arrested Roger Louis. Delaney was only twenty-one, just old enough to serve, and he had been with the sheriff only two or three months when he made this arrest. Delaney is a farm boy from a family in the western end of the county. They have a nice farm, flat land or reasonably so for this country, and they keep a good herd of dairy cattle. Necessarily they are hard-working people, and the parents demand that their children contribute their share of the sweat from the time they are old enough to help. Bob didn't like farm work. He enlisted in the Navy as soon as he was old enough and his father consented. His father consented, thinking Bob would go out and see enough of the world to last him the rest of his life and would then return home and work the land as God and his father intended. But Bob's reaction was different. In the Navy he became a shore patrolman, and when he was discharged he thought he was trained for police work. He thought about landing a job with the police force of some city, but he was still enough of an Ohio hilliken to return to Marshall County and ask for a deputy's job. His father tolerates it because he keeps thinking Bob will tire of it and come back to the farm, but everyone else knows it will never happen. Bob is a blond youngster with a handsome face and figure, married to a sixteen-year-old beauty who quit high school to become his wife. She is pregnant now, of course. Bob is tanned, and his tan contrasts with his light hair, which he cuts very short and neat. His wife cuts down his shirt tails to fit closely around his waist, just like the chief of police has his wife do for him. Garson would like to have Bob on the Alexandria police force, but it is said that Bob is too ambitious. The rumors say Bob will run for sheriff when he thinks he is old enough to take it away from George, and if he were on the police force he would want the chief's job. Well, you can't blame a young man for being ambitious.

When he had stated his name and address for the record, Bob was asked if he was with Handschumacher when Roger Louis was arrested, and he said, "Yes, I took Handschumacher with me when I went out on that call." He wanted the record straight about who went with whom.

"Where did you find the suspect?"

"Walking on Pine Tree Road about a mile from the house where the sheriff caught the girl."

"Did he offer any resistance?"

"No, we drove up beside him and asked him if he was Roger Louis, and he said he was. I told him he would have to come with us, so he got in the car."

"Did he talk to you on the way back to town?"

"A little, yes."

"What, if anything, did he say about Ruth Gibson?"

"He said something about how she had got him into this trouble."

"Do you remember his exact words?"

"No, sir. Only that he said something about how he wouldn't be in such a mess if it hadn't been for her."

"What did you do with him when you got him back to town?" asked Baumgardner quietly. Heads turned and people sat up because Baumgardner had *not* asked the question they expected.

"We searched him, took his stuff from him, and put him in a cell until the sheriff could get back and question him."

"Is the man you arrested and brought in present in the court-room?"

"Yes, that's him sitting over there," Bob Delaney said casually. He was completely at his ease as a witness.

"Okay, that's all. You may cross-examine."

MacInroth rose and crossed the front of the courtroom to his customary place at the rail of the jury box. "When you were bringing the suspect in, riding in your car, what did he say about Paul Russell?"

"I didn't hear him say anything about Russell." It was plain from his manner that he knew he was contradicting Handschumacher on an important point.

Everyone looked at Baumgardner. The prosecutor was not surprised. He had known what Delaney would say. They had been over it several times.

"Well now," MacInroth went on, exercising his every talent to make the question sound significant, "you were in the car with Louis and Handschumacher, and it is not likely, is it, that they could have said anything you couldn't hear?"

"No," said Delaney calmly.

"Well, are you aware that Deputy Handschumacher testified that he heard Roger Louis say he was sorry he had not shot Paul Russell?"

"I know he says that's what Louis said, but I didn't hear it," said Delaney.

"Is it your testimony, then, that it was not said?"

"I didn't hear it."

"Could it have been said without your hearing it?"

"I don't see how."

"Well," said MacInroth, and he could not restrain a broad grin. He went back to his table and picked up his notes. Then, standing at his table, he asked, "Did you put handcuffs on Roger Louis when you arrested him?"

"Handschumacher did."

"Was that before you got him in the car, or after?"

"After we got him in the car. He got right in the car when I told him he would have to go with us. He got in the back seat— we were in the front—and Handschumacher got the handcuffs out of the glove compartment. He told Louis to put up his hands, and he put them on him."

"Did either you or Handschumacher get out of the car to arrest Roger Louis?"

"No, I just told him to get in the car, and he did."

"Did he complain about being arrested?"

"Yes, he said we were crazy to arrest him."

"Was that before, or after, he got in the car?"

"While he was getting in."

"All right. That's all. And thank you, Bob," said MacInroth with a smile.

Baumgardner did not want to question Delaney further, and he left the courtroom.

"Now," said Baumgardner, rising, "I request that the jury be taken to view the county jail, your Honor."

MacInroth spoke up. "We would like to know the purpose of this request, your Honor."

"A fact, or rather an event, material to the state's case occurred in the county jail, if it please the court," said Joe Baumgardner. "It is my thought that the jury can better understand the testimony they are to hear if they see the jail."

"We object," said MacInroth. "This is not within the purview of the statute which allows a jury to be taken to view the premises." Bob Day was thumbing furiously through a copy of Page's *Ohio Revised Code*, and MacInroth waited until Day was able to hand him the bright red volume open to the right section. "If the court please, no material fact occurred at the county jail. Section 2945.16 of the *Revised Code* authorizes a view of the premises where a material fact occurred. Obviously that means where an element of the alleged crime is supposed to have occurred. In the case of *Jones vs. State*, the Supreme Court said that the court of common pleas can send the jury out to view the premises where the crime was committed. That does not mean they can be sent anywhere it is convenient for the prosecution to send them to bolster some element of its case. If the state wants to take the jury to see the store where this alleged crime took place, that is one thing. To go anywhere else is not authorized by law."

Joe Baumgardner stayed on his feet while MacInroth spoke, and when MacInroth sat down, he said, "Your Honor, Mr. Mac-

140

Inroth reads the annotation in the *Code* correctly. He would be better enlightened on the law if he would read the case. He has quoted the wording of the annotation correctly, but that is not the point of the case. I have the case here for your Honor—and defense counsel if they choose—to see."

"Come up here," said Judge Kemp, beckoning with a finger.

The three attorneys went up to the bench, Baumgardner carrying the brown volume of *Ohio State Reports*. The judge took the book and looked at the case for several minutes while the attorneys waited. Then MacInroth and Day looked at the book momentarily. There was a short discussion, which I could not hear, and the lawyers went back to their places.

"I can't say that the law is too clear on this point," said the judge uneasily. "However, I fail to see any harm in having the jury view the jail. The defense reserves its exception, of course." He swung his big chair around to face the jury. "Now, ladies and gentlemen, you are going to be taken to look at the county jail because, supposedly, some event of significance to this case took place there. The fact that you are going out to look at the jail does not of itself mean that anything important happened there. Whether it did and whether it was important, if it did, is for you to decide from the evidence you hear about it. Now, while you are out looking at the jail, no one is to talk to you about the case. The bailiff and someone from the sheriff's office will conduct you through the jail, and they are not to talk to you except to point out what is what. You should not ask any questions or expect any answers. As always when you leave the courtroom, you should not discuss the case with anyone. The court will recess for twenty minutes while the jury is taken to view the jail."

Quentin stepped before the jury box and asked the jurors to remain in their seats while he went to find an attendant to take them through the jail. The spectators went out the back doors of the courtroom in a hurry and nearly cleared the room. The attorneys kept their seats, and the judge came over to me, shaking his head.

"I don't know whether I should have allowed that or not," he said.

"Well," I told him, "I don't know what the law says, if anything, but I'm like you in that I can't see any harm in it."

"I don't know that it proves anything. MacInroth is afraid it will prejudice them against the girl if they see the jail. I'm inclined to the view it would more likely tend to make them sympathize with her. I don't know." He went on out, headed for the men's room.

Quentin came back from the sheriff's office after a few minutes. He had Handschumacher with him. MacInroth immediately went over to Baumgardner's table, complaining. Quentin went out again and came back with the sheriff himself. Then the jurors were led out of the courtroom and off on their errand. The attorneys and the two defendants waited at their places. Day conferred animatedly with Ruth Gibson, while MacInroth listened.

Bill Mullen, who was sitting with me again this morning, said to me, "I would like to know what Baumgardner has in mind."

"Well, ask him," I said, and since Baumgardner happened to be looking our way, I beckoned, and he walked over to join us.

"What's going on?" Mullen asked.

"Trial," said Baumgardner jovially, casting me a meaningful glance.

"What's viewing the jail got to do with it, if you don't mind my asking?" Bill persisted.

"Oh, you'll see," said Baumgardner. "You'll see. Our little bird has done some singing back there."

"I think they've got that figured out," Bill said, nodding toward the defense table where the girl and the attorneys were still talking.

"Possibly so," Baumgardner said. "Got a cigar you could lend me, Judge?"

"Glad to be of service," I said, and I gave him a cigar and a light.

"How soon will you finish your case?" Bill asked.

Baumgardner rolled the cigar in his fingers and looked at the thick smoke curling off the end of it. "Before noon," he said. "Providing, of course, they don't cross-examine too much."

"Do you think they'll put the defendants on the stand?"

"I don't see how they can avoid it," Baumgardner shrugged.

"Well, I'm going to have to get over to the office before long and give them something to print," said Bill. "I hope your jury is getting an eyeful."

What the jury was seeing was not unusual. The jail is on the second floor of the annex building behind the courthouse on the square. It is a reasonably strong jail, though a few people have managed to saw out of it, and we have had to call in a welder from time to time to repair bars cut by men who tried, as well as by men who succeeded. The main jail will accommodate about fifty men, two to a cell in twenty cells, and ten in bunks set up when necessary in the main cage of the cell block. In the old courthouse jail we used before the annex was built about 1925 there was no place for women. In the day when the courthouse was built women were not put in jail, I suppose. But by 1925 they were occasionally, and two cells were provided for them on the first floor of the building, in a room behind the sheriff's apartment. By the 1940's we found those two cells inadequate. A bricklayer and some welders were brought in to build a women's jail on the second floor in space occupied by a small apartment formerly intended for the jailer. There are four cells in line along one wall of the bricked-in room. At the far end of this narrow room there is a shower. At the near end a wall of steel bars separates the women's jail from the open corridor leading to the stairway. Opening onto this corridor also is another barred wall and the entrance to the men's jail, the main jail. So long as the prisoners are locked in their cells the men and women cannot see each other or communicate, except by shouting, but when they are out of their cells they can stand at their respective bars and talk across. They are separated by about fifteen feet. This Joe Baumgardner had sent the jury to see: the prisoners could talk from one part of the jail to another.

When the jury returned, Judge Kemp reopened the session with some words of his own.

"I would like," he said, "a stipulation by counsel that the defendants and their attorneys waived their right to accompany the jury on its view of the jail. You had a statutory right to go but did not go."

"We do not want to waive our objection to the entire procedure, your Honor," said MacInroth.

"You may reserve your objection to my allowing the jury to

view the jail, but I would like a statement in the record that you did not take advantage of your statutory right to go with the jury to view the premises only because you chose not to do so."

MacInroth rose. "It may be stipulated for my client that, while we reserve our objection to the whole procedure, we do waive our right to accompany the jury on its view."

"Thank you," said the judge.

Bob Day, without rising, said, "We join in the stipulation, your Honor."

"Thank you. Mr. Baumgardner, will you proceed?"

"Call Chloe Adams," said the prosecuting attorney.

Chloe Adams works in the sheriff's office. She is a young woman of about thirty, married and divorced and the mother of a little daughter of about ten years whom she supports. She is a bleached blonde and faintly attractive, though she has protruding front teeth. She wears spectacles with upswept corners. Usually she dresses in a gray skirt and a black blouse and wears a little gold deputy's badge on the blouse. She answers the telephone, does the typing, makes calls on the radio, and, together with the sheriff's wife, she handles the women's jail.

After she was identified for the record, Joe Baumgardner had Chloe describe her duties, and then he asked her, "Are you acquainted with the defendant Ruth Gibson?"

"Yes, sir."

"When did you first meet her?"

"Well, I eat over at Reitlinger's sometimes, and I had seen her working in there, but I didn't become acquainted with her until she was brought in and put in jail."

"On May twentieth of this year?"

"Yes, sir."

"How often do you see her?"

"Every day."

"In the jail?"

"Yes, sir."

"Now tell me, Chloe, is Ruth Gibson kept in one of the cells or is she allowed to run at large in the cell block?"

"She is kept in a cell most of the time now."

"Was she allowed the run of the jail at first?"

"Yes, sir."

"Why the change?"

"She talked too much with the men over across the hall."

"Objection!" said Bob Day emphatically. "That is irrelevant and prejudicial."

"Sustained," said the judge. "The jury will ignore the comment about the defendant's talking to the men."

"In any case," said Baumgardner, "she was for some time allowed to remain outside a cell, is that right?"

"Yes, sir."

"And outside a cell she could communicate with men in the men's jail, if she chose to do so?"

"Yes, sir."

"And now she is confined in a cell?"

"Well, not all the time. We go up and put her in before we close the office. During the day she is out, but at night she is in a cell."

"And when did you change the practice?"

"I'm not sure when it was. After she had been up there about six weeks or so."

"In July? About then?"

"About then, yes."

"All right. That's all. Thank you."

"No questions," said Bob Day, and Chloe was dismissed.

"Call Horace Miller," said Joe Baumgardner. This set up a stir in the courtroom. Everyone was wondering who the witness would be, and now that his name had been mentioned no one seemed to know who he was. People turned to each other, and shrugs were exchanged all over the room.

Quentin returned with the witness. Horace Miller is known in Alexandria as Tom Miller, and Tom Miller is known to everyone. He is known because, a few years ago—ten years ago, I suppose it was—he played football and basketball for Alexandria High School and was probably the most skillful all-around athlete the the town has ever seen. To some people this glory never fades. It has faded for Tom, but to a great many people that is no matter; to them he will always be something of a hero, no matter what he does, no matter what he becomes. It makes no difference that he went to college on an athletic scholarship and promptly flunked out; he still is the boy who ran the ball back ninety-six yards after a last-quarter punt by Bellaire, winning the game and completing an undefeated season for Alexandria. That he became a problem drinker, and still is, means nothing to people who remember him shooting baskets from all over the floor, scoring thirty points per game and keeping it up for three seasons. He was rejected by the Army because of a knee injury he received on the football field, tried to become a professional boxer and only succeeded in getting his nose broken badly, and has never held a job more than six months since he graduated from high school. Now he makes his living as rack boy in the local poolroom and picks up extra money from time to time doing odd jobs; but all this has not dimmed his glory in the slightest among the athletic-minded. They still call him a hero. They still talk about him, tell of his exploits, discuss his records, admire him. He is sufficiently intelligent to know the truth about himself, and in that he is more intelligent than one element of the community.

Miller walked to the witness stand and took his seat. He is still broad-shouldered and muscular, though he has acquired a belly he did not have as a star athlete, and he is going to lose his hair before many more years. His face was always gross, never handsome, and the broken nose disfigures him. He was wearing faded blue jeans and a white shirt.

"State your name, please," said Joe Baumgardner.

"Horace Miller."

"Known as Tom Miller?"

"Yes."

"Where do you live, Tom?"

"I've got a room over on Bridge Street."

"Are you acquainted with the defendant in this case, Ruth Gibson?"

"Yes."

"How well do you know her?"

"Pretty well."

"How well is that, Tom?"

"I've taken her out a few times." Miller had no expression. I mean there was no expression on his face and none in his voice.

146

If his manner revealed anything, he would be an unwilling witness, because he was subpoenaed, not eager to cooperate but afraid to tell anything but the truth.

"When did you last see her, Tom?"

"Back in June."

"Where did you see her?"

"Up in the jail."

"Were you in jail?"

"Yes."

"What for?"

"Drunk and disorderly."

"How long were you there?"

"About a week."

"And where was she?"

"She was in jail too."

"In the women's jail?"

"Yes."

"And you were in the men's jail and could see her and talk to her. Is that right?"

"Yes," Miller said. The jury knew that he could see her and talk to her. They had visited the jail and had seen how men in their section could easily converse with the inmates in the women's section. That was Joe Baumgardner's purpose in showing them the jail.

"What did you and she talk about?"

"Different things. A lot of things."

"How about the robbery? Did she talk about that?"

"Yes."

"What did she say?"

"She said she didn't do it."

"How's that?" asked Baumgardner, and he stood up.

"She said she didn't do it," repeated Miller.

Baumgardner opened his file and took out a stapled paper consisting of three or four sheets. Looking at the paper, he asked, "Did you ever ask her whether she really did it? Did you ask her, 'Level with me now, honey, did you or didn't you do it?'"

"Yes."

"You asked her that? In those words?"

147

"Yes."

"And what did she say?"

"She said she didn't do it," repeated Miller insistently.

Baumgardner walked up to the witness stand and faced his witness. "Mr. Miller," he said, "did you come to my office and give me a statement about this case?"

"Yes."

"Did I have your statement typed up for you?"

"Yes."

"Well," said Baumgardner, thrusting the paper toward Miller, "is that your signature there?"

"Objection," said MacInroth. "Can we see that paper?"

Baumgardner crossed the front of the courtroom and tossed the paper on the table in front of MacInroth.

"Your Honor," Bob Day rose and said after he and MacInroth had studied the paper a moment, "we object to any use of this paper in evidence. It is not a sworn statement, not a deposition. It was taken out of our presence, and besides, the witness is here to testify."

"Approach the bench," said the judge.

There was a conference lasting several minutes, and though none of us could hear, angry disagreement was apparent. Then the lawyers went back to their seats.

"The court will permit the question," said Judge Kemp. "The defense reserves its objection."

Baumgardner went to the bench, took the paper, and returned to the witness with it. "Now, Mr. Miller," he said, "the question is, is that your signature at the end of the paper?"

"Yes," Miller said quietly.

"Is this, then, the statement you signed in my office?"

"Objection—for reasons already stated," said Bob Day.

"You may answer," said the judge.

"Yes, that is my statement."

"Are these, then, your words? Quote: 'I asked her . . .'"

"We object for reasons already stated," Bob Day persisted.

"Overruled."

"Quote: 'I asked her, Level with me now, honey, did you or

didn't you do it?' Are those the words you put in your statement, Mr. Miller?"

"Yes."

"Objection, and move that it be stricken."

"Overruled."

"And then, Mr. Miller, did you go on in your statement to say this? 'She said . . .' "

"Objection."

"Overruled."

It was mechanical by now. Bob Day spoke somewhat grimly, making his objections, knowing that he was getting them into the record but that the questions and answers were going to continue in spite of him. Baumgardner was patient with the interruptions. The judge was manifestly uneasy. He should have been because, in my opinion at least, he was ruling incorrectly.

"To go on, Mr. Miller," said Baumgardner. " 'She said, What do you think, Tommy?' Is that your statement? Is that correctly read from your statement?"

"Objection."

"Overruled."

"Yes."

"All right," said Baumgardner, now returning to his table and tossing down the paper which contained the statement. "Between the time you made this statement in my office and today when you testified under oath, you have changed your story, haven't you?"

"Yes," said Miller blandly.

"Well, tell us if you will, then, what is the nature of the relationship between you and this girl? What would make you lie for her now?"

"Objection," said Bob Day, this time excitedly. "Now this is his witness, your Honor, not ours. He called him; we didn't. Now he doesn't like what his witness says, so he wants to impeach him. Well, it is fundamental that you can't impeach your own witness. Or to put it less elegantly, the prosecutor is stuck with what his witness says."

Joe Baumgardner sat down and began to study his notes while the judge considered the objection.

"The objection is sustained," said the judge finally.

"I have no further questions to ask of this witness," said Joe Baumgardner contemptuously.

"And I don't believe we'd care to cross-examine," said Bob Day.

Miller hurried from the stand. Ruth Gibson turned to Day and spoke to him quietly while Miller left. He looked at her before he went through the door, but she was intent on what she was saying to her lawyer and did not notice him.

"Call James F. Pucket," said Baumgardner.

A gray-haired man of some sixty years, wearing a blue business suit, came in and took the stand. Under Baumgardner's questioning he identified himself as accountant and payroll officer of the Caesar's Creek Plant of Gardner Metals Corporation.

"Now, Mr. Pucket, have you, pursuant to my request, checked your payroll records for information concerning the employment of Roger Louis?"

"Yes, sir, I have," said Mr. Pucket.

"How long do your records show that Louis has been employed by your company?"

"Two years and about seven months."

"During that time has he worked steadily?"

"Yes, sir. He was laid off for three months in 1960 because the plant was not in full production during that period, and he was out on strike with the rest of the employees for eight days in January of 1961. Other than that he has worked steadily."

"What have been his average weekly earnings during that period while he worked for you?"

"Averaging only the weeks when he worked, and not averaging in the weeks when he was laid off or on strike, his weekly earnings have run in the neighborhood of sixty-five dollars per week take-home pay after deductions."

"In other words, he takes home more than two hundred and fifty dollars per month?"

"Yes."

"What were his weekly earnings in May of 1961?"

"A little more than that. He was making about eighty-two dollars per week then."

"On how many occasions during the period when he was employed with you have his wages been attached by creditors?"

"Objection," said MacInroth. "It is irrelevant and prejudicial."

"If the court please," said Baumgardner, "it is my intention to show motive by establishing that this defendant has been desperate for money."

"Objection overruled," said the judge.

"During the period while he has been employed by us," said Mr. Pucket carefully, referring to notes he had in his hand, "the corporation has been served with garnishments eleven times."

"Eleven times?"

"That is right."

"Referring to the months immediately preceding the crime here charged, that is to say, in April, March, February, and January of 1961, how many times were his wages attached?"

"His wages were attached by creditors in each of the months you mentioned—in January, February, March, and April."

"But not in May?"

"No, not since April."

"How much was taken by his creditors and how much left to him?"

"Well, under the amended law, an unmarried person, not the head of a household, is allowed to keep only one hundred dollars exempt, so each month we paid Louis one hundred dollars and turned over the balance of his earnings, in varying amounts, to the Alexandria Municipal Court."

"Who filed these attachments?"

"Referring to those four attachments only, there were two creditors. In January it was a gasoline station, Peter Showalter, doing business as Pete's Service Stop. In each of the other months it was Steady Finance Company."

"Has your company any policy with respect to firing an employee who has too many attachments?"

"Yes, our contract with the union says we can let them go after three cases, but we don't ordinarily do it unless the thing becomes chronic."

"Had you given Roger Louis any warning?"

"Yes, after the April garnishment came in I called him in and told him that the company could not put up with it any longer, that it costs us too much in extra accounting work. I told him that I was authorized to say that if it happened again we would have to let him go."

"And when was that?"

"I'm not certain of the date. It was about the first of May."

"Thank you very much, Mr. Pucket. That's all."

MacInroth did not rise. "Mr. Pucket," he said, "has Roger Louis had a good work record except for these garnishments?"

"I suppose so, yes."

"Never any disciplinary problem?"

"Not to my knowledge. That is outside my department."

"You say his earnings have increased during the period he has been with you?"

"Yes, they have."

"Steadily?"

"Yes."

"I believe that's all, thank you."

The witness rose, but Baumgardner stopped him with a motion of his hand. "One thing more, Mr. Pucket. These increases in pay—do they represent promotions or just the regular increases that go with service?"

"Our wage contract is such that a man's wages increase automatically during his length of service. Besides that, we had a new contract negotiation, and Louis benefited from the increase that the union won there."

"Thank you again. That's all." Baumgardner glanced at his notes and then said, "Call Peter Showalter."

Showalter came in. He was a man of about forty, dressed in the uniform of a service-station attendant.

"State your full name, please."

"Peter Showalter."

"Your address?"

"I live at 814 River Street in Alexandria."

"What is your business, Mr. Showalter?"

"I lease a service station from Sohio."

"What do you call it?"

"Pete's Sohio Service Stop."

"Where is it located?"

"Out by Caesar Creek, by the plant."

"Is one of your customers Roger Louis?"

"He used to be."

"When he did business with you did you extend credit to him?"

"Yes, sir."

"Did he pay you?"

"Well, he got so he didn't."

"Did you attach his wages in January of this year?"

"Yes, sir."

"How much did he owe you at that time?"

"Three hundred and eighty-four dollars and some cents."

"Was all that for gasoline and oil?"

"No, sir."

"What was it for?"

"Well, he'd wrote me a bad check."

"Objection!" said MacInroth strongly.

"It will be overruled, Mr. MacInroth," said the court. "The jury is instructed that this is to be considered as evidence only of the defendant's need for money, not for any other purpose."

"Under what circumstances did you take his check?" asked Baumgardner.

"He wrote checks pretty often in my station. For cash. Sometimes I cashed his pay check too. Well, he come in on a Saturday night in December—I don't remember which Saturday—and wanted me to cash a check for two hundred dollars. I said I wouldn't do it. He already owed me nearly two hundred for gas and oil and tires. But he said he'd pay me off for all of it if I'd let him have this, and he hung around and argued about it, so finally I let him have it. But when I sent the check in, the bank sent it back."

"So what did you do?"

"Well, I took it to my lawyer, Mr. Jones, and he sued on it and my bills too, and attached his wages for it."

"The attachment didn't cover it all, did it?"

"No, he come in after his wages had been attached and give me the balance. He said his dad give him the money."

"Did you threaten him with criminal prosecution?"

"Objection."

"It will be admitted as going to the defendant's need for money."

"What was the question?" the witness asked.

"After Louis wrote you a bad check, did you ever threaten him with criminal prosecution?"

"He called me after I had his wages attached and asked me why I wanted to do that to him, and I told him he was lucky I hadn't turned that check over to the prosecutor."

"Thank you. That's all."

MacInroth leaned across his table, resting himself on his folded arms, and he smiled at the witness and asked, "You didn't say to Roger Louis that you would prosecute him if he didn't pay you the rest of the money, did you?"

"No, I didn't say that."

"You didn't then threaten him with prosecution, did you?"

"No, not exactly."

"That's all."

"Call Donald Porter," said Baumgardner as Showalter went out.

I know Don, of course. He works for the Citizens and Farmers Bank of Alexandria—has for forty years, and he looks like one of the little men who work down in the bowels of a bank. If he wore sleeve garters and a green eye shade, it would complete the image he creates. He took the stand and identified himself as the bank's chief accountant.

"I want to talk to you about the account of Roger Louis," said Baumgardner. "Have you brought the ledger sheet?"

"Yes, this is it," said Don. He had it in his coat pocket and took it out.

Baumgardner took the sheet and handed it to the reporter. "May this be marked as 'State's Exhibit A' please," he said, and when it was marked he took it over to the defense table for examination by MacInroth and Day. Then he brought it to the witness. "Will you identify the piece of paper which has been marked 'State's Exhibit A' please?"

"This," said Don, "is the ledger sheet of the account of Roger Louis for the period from October, 1960, through March, 1961."

Baumgardner reached out and took the sheet again. "We ask

that this be received in evidence as 'State's Exhibit A,'" he said, and he passed the sheet to the judge.

"We object to it," said MacInroth.

"It will be received for the same purpose, that is, to show motive," said Judge Kemp.

Baumgardner retrieved the sheet from the judge and returned it to the witness. "Does that ledger sheet accurately reflect the balance in his account on December first?"

"It does."

"What was the balance in the Roger Louis account on December first, 1960?"

"Eighteen dollars and fifty-two cents."

Baumgardner turned to the defense attorneys. "Will you gentlemen stipulate that December first was a Thursday and that the first Saturday in December was the third, and that there were Saturdays on the tenth, seventeenth, twenty-fourth, and thirty-first?"

We waited while Day took a pocket calendar from his billfold, and then the two defense lawyers agreed.

"Just going back a little, what was the highest balance in this account during the month of November, 1960?"

"On November third there was seventy-eight dollars and two cents in the account. That was the highest balance in November."

"And what was the highest balance in December?"

"Twenty-four dollars and twenty-four cents."

"And in January, 1961—the highest balance?"

"Two dollars and fourteen cents."

"At any time during those three months did Roger Louis have two hundred dollars on deposit?"

"No."

"One hundred dollars?"

"No."

"If he wrote a check for two hundred dollars in December it had to bounce, didn't it?"

"It certainly did."

"Is there a two-hundred-dollar check shown in December?"

"Yes, a check for two hundred dollars came in on December thirteenth."

"What was on deposit at the time that check came in?"

"Twenty-four dollars and twenty-four cents."

"So the account was overdrawn—?"

"One hundred seventy-five dollars and seventy-six cents."

"What did the bank do with that check?"

"We returned it to the payee."

"Yes, thank you. That will be all."

"No questions," said MacInroth.

While Don Porter made his way to the door, Joe Baumgardner studied his notes. He shuffled through them hastily, then gathered them up, struck their edges on the table to straighten them, and placed them in their manila folder. Closing the folder, he pushed it aside, and, looking up at the judge, said, "The state rests."

VII

WHEN THE STATE rested its case, the judge recessed the court until one-thirty.

I walked to the defense table. I put my hand on Bob Day's shoulder and said, "Well, now you know what you have to fight. You know the worst."

Bob quickly got up and offered me his chair, and since I was ninety-one years old I took it. He sat on the table between me and his client, and John Kimball MacInroth himself turned around to talk to us, since Louis had already departed to join his father.

"Judge, there's not much point in an introduction here," said Bob, "but I would like to introduce you to Ruth. This is Judge William Applegate, Ruth. He was judge for fifty years before Judge Kemp."

"Hello," the girl said, courteously and quietly.

"Well, I wish you luck, young lady," I said. You have to be inanely polite from time to time. Of course, I actually did wish her luck. I always sympathize with defendants—almost always, anyway.

"I guess I'm going to need a lot of luck," she said.

"Oh, maybe not, maybe not," I said. "You're being well represented."

Bob Day grinned. "We'll see about that when the jury comes back."

"I represented a fellow once," said MacInroth, "who was accused of stealing a car. I was appointed by the court, like Bob. He was about the guiltiest man I ever saw. The trial was an ordeal. He didn't have a chance, but I did what I could. When the jury went out I knew he was going to be convicted, and he must have known too. So I said to him, 'Are you satisfied, anyway, that I did the best that could be done for you?' And he said, 'If I get off, you did a good job for me, buddy. If I don't, you're a son of a bitch, you son of a bitch.'"

The girl smiled, and Bob said to her, "I hope you will be calling me something nice when it's over."

"I will," she said with a mischievous little grin, "even if I have to say it in a letter from the reformatory."

"God forbid," said Bob, shaking his head.

"Well, I wish we could take you to lunch with us," said MacInroth, looking around for Chloe or the sheriff's wife to come for the girl. He was hungry.

"So do I," she said.

"Is the food bad?" I asked.

She shrugged. "Not bad. Kind of monotonous is all. People are nice. My family brings me things, and Billy sends over snacks from the restaurant."

"Billy sent her a radio too," Bob said.

"Yes," she said. "That's a big help."

Chloe came in, and Ruth got up. She ran her hands down across her legs to straighten her skirt.

"A little lipstick, remember," Bob said to her.

"Okay," she said. "I'm glad to meet you, sir," she told me, and in that "sir" I thought she betrayed herself a bit. "I'll see you after lunch, Bob."

Bob nodded, and he watched her go to join Chloe to be taken back to jail. For a moment I thought Bob was going to be more than ordinarily unhappy if his client went to prison.

Bob Day turned to me. He drew his lower lip in between his teeth just a little, and he chuckled beneath his breath. "She doesn't seem like the type, does she?" Then he nodded and went on, "Well, she is. I mean she's a flirt. Did you notice the sheriff and all those deputies? She's got herself a group of admirers in her jailers. She'd like to have another in her lawyer."

"She wouldn't have to work hard to arrange it," said MacInroth.

"Is that why you've had her dressed like a scarecrow?" I asked.

"No, yesterday she just showed up that way. She doesn't have any more taste than that."

"She's not pretty with her clothes on," said MacInroth.

"I didn't know you had seen her without them," laughed Bob.

"I haven't," MacInroth was quick to assert.

"She's sort of what you'd call an earthy beauty," said Bob, smiling broadly and looking down at the table. "You ought to see her up there in the jail. She wears that pair of shorts that impressed Mike Bradstreet so much, and she lets her hair hang in strings. Of course it's been hot up there this summer—"

"Is that why they had to get her away from the door?" I asked.

"I guess so," said Bob. "I guess the sight of her was driving some of the men in the men's section out of their minds." Then he became serious and said, "Really, though, she's not a bad girl at all, for all I can find out, considering the class of people she comes from. She's no *femme fatale*. Not by a damn sight. The loafers on the corners would like to have it that way, but she isn't. I think she's pretty ordinary. I think she's pretty much what you'd expect in a girl from her background and at her age."

"She's not really pretty," said MacInroth.

"You don't like her, do you, John?" I said.

MacInroth leaned back in his chair. "No, it's not that I don't like her," he explained. "It's just that she's a complicating factor in this case. I could defend him better without her. That's my feeling about her."

"I take it," I said, "that there is no affection lost between her and Louis any more."

"Well," said MacInroth, "his father keeps telling him he wouldn't be in trouble except for her. Roger thinks she did plot the robbery with Russell, so when Russell was robbed he immediately thinks of her, which leads the sheriff to whatever guy she is going with at the moment. Roger thinks it's his misfortune to look something like the guy who did it. That's what Roger thinks happened."

"Of course, she thinks he's let her down," said Bob. "She had the idea his family should put up her bond too, and they didn't, and she resents every day she spends in jail as being his fault. I talked her out of that pretty well, but not entirely. Then, of course, he has never come to see her or anything. And besides that, one of the Louis clan told her father that his whore daughter got Roger in trouble. That was too much."

"Either one of them would be glad to see the other get convicted," said MacInroth.

"Well, I don't think *she's* that bitter," Bob said.

"He is," said MacInroth. "And of course the fate of each is tied to the fate of the other."

I laughed. "So you two have to keep them from ratting on each other."

"No," said MacInroth seriously. "There's nothing to rat about."

"Well, I'm hungry," said Bob. "My wife is waiting for me. Judge, would you have lunch with Betty and me? You too, John."

I had been planning to have lunch with my usual associates, but you cannot turn down an invitation like that. Both John and I agreed, and we went out to meet Mrs. Day. As I have mentioned before, Bob's wife is an extraordinarily attractive young woman, and she has the money to do whatever a well-off young woman wants. She has the kind of education that makes her able to talk intelligently on a variety of subjects. She really does not belong in a town this size.

The Days, Bob's family, are not from Alexandria. His father came here as general manager of one of the plants up the river, and when he retired he decided to stay in Alexandria. Bob returned here after his graduation from Michigan Law School, because he wanted to be near his family, I suppose. Otherwise, I cannot understand why a well-bred young man would set up business so far from what you might expect would interest him.

Of course, Betty might have made him come back. Her family has lived here since the Indians left. Greene is the name—related,

I have heard, to the General Greene of the Revolutionary War, though they say they are not. Anyway, they have been in Marshall County since the first settlement at Marietta was founded. They were landowners, of course, and had big tracts along the river and back in the hills. They sold their land, and their second generation was mostly doctors and lawyers and judges. Some of the later generations soured and did not improve the family reputation, and others moved away, but three families still live in Alexandria. Betty's family still owns and lives in the old brick house built before the Civil War by Jonathan Greene, the lawyer and judge who wrote a history of Ohio. Betty met Bob shortly after his family moved here; they were high school sweethearts. He went to the University of Michigan and she went East to school, but they came home for the summers. When he graduated from Michigan they were married, and she went to Ann Arbor and worked and helped put him through law school, even though both families had enough money to support them. Her father has since died and left her a considerable estate, including the big brick house where her mother still lives. Bob also has some money of his own. They still need the income from his practice, but they have a nice cushion behind them. Bob is a member of the country club and plays golf as much as he can. They entertain a great deal. They have two little daughters, both dark-haired and pretty like their mother.

Betty Greene Day was waiting for us outside the courtroom, and we walked together up the street to the Alexandria Bar and Grill. Of course, we did not join my cronies at the big table but took instead a small table for four.

"I see you met my husband's client, Judge Applegate," said Betty to me. "Do you think I am in any danger of his falling in love with her?"

The thought had momentarily occurred to me, and I am afraid my face told her as much. "An infatuation perhaps," I said, as facetiously as I could, "but I don't think you are in any danger of losing him to her."

"Particularly in view of the fact that she is apt to spend the next eight years, at a minimum, in the reformatory for women," said Bob.

John MacInroth was studying the menu with absorbing interest, but he looked up long enough to say, "Let's be optimistic at least at lunch."

"I don't think you have much reason to be," said Betty. "I'm sorry, but I thought Joe Baumgardner had the ends tied up pretty firmly."

"We never decide a case without hearing the defense," I said.

"I don't know," said MacInroth. "It will only confuse the jury, who, I have no doubt, are now thoroughly convinced of the guilt of both of them."

"I really expected it to be worse," said Bob. "I thought the prosecution's case would surprise us more than it did."

"Handschumacher surprised you," I said.

Bob Day laughed. "Yes, and Miller surprised Joe Baumgardner."

"It would help if your sullen friend would not look so sullen," Betty said to MacInroth.

"He's an angry young man, that one," said MacInroth.

"They don't seem to make a very likely couple," I said.

"Oh, wait till you hear the testimony for the defense," said Betty with a short laugh.

"There is just one thing I wish I had done," said MacInroth, who had suddenly lapsed into thoughtfulness. "I wish I had subpoenaed that damned police chief."

"You had better explain that to the judge," said Bob. "The way it stands that remark is absolutely incomprehensible."

MacInroth turned toward me and said, "Oh. Sorry. I guess you can't read minds. I was reading in the crime bulletins they get up in the sheriff's office about a fellow who was captured over by Columbus in a town over there. Town of—uh— Well, anyway," he went on impatiently, "I read in the bulletin that a fellow was captured over there who sort of fits the description of our robber. Dark and medium-sized and all; held up a store with a gun. He was driving a Pennsylvania car, and he might have driven through here and pulled this robbery and then gone on and pulled another one and got caught. It's not at all likely, but it is a possibility. So I wrote the chief of police over there and asked him about this fellow he has in custody. No answer. Then I called him. He wouldn't talk about it. Said it was police business. I should have subpoenaed him."

"He wouldn't have made you much of a witness," I said.

"No, but I could have made him come down here and sit in the courthouse on a bench for two or three days. I could have subpoenaed him and then not called him to the stand. That's what I should have done."

"Maybe you should have at that," I said. "Though I doubt the lesson would have soaked through his thick policeman's skull."

"Let me make a speech," said MacInroth. "If the prosecutor had had any reason to think a man in custody in Columbus or Cleveland or Cincinnati might be of some help to him in this case, he could have gotten him here to testify without the slightest difficulty. If he suspected a piece of evidence might be found somewhere, anywhere, he could round up a dozen men to go hunting for it for him. If he needed help preparing his case, the police department, the sheriff's department, the highway patrol, even the FBI would all help him. If the defense needs a piece of evidence, the defense can dig it up the best way it can and at its own expense. And don't tell me about private investigators, because no one but the very wealthy can afford them."

"Well, at least you have a client who is paying the bills," said Betty. "Bob has already spent the hundred dollars the county will pay him for defending this girl. He's doing his work for nothing, or, worse, it's going to cost him money."

"I don't mind that so much," said Bob. "That's part of being a lawyer. I don't mind doing my job for nothing occasionally for somebody who needs it and can't afford it. But if we needed to pay a witness's fare to get in here from Texas or someplace, or if we needed a laboratory examination of some evidence, or if we needed something else that costs money, where would we get the money to pay for it?"

"The court has the authority to allow you something toward those expenses," I said.

"After you've paid them," Bob said. "And maybe you've spent the money on wild goose chases. How far can the court go with that?"

John MacInroth spoke up again. "How many times have we

defended some wretch who tells us that we could get him off if we would just get Joe to testify for him. What's Joe's last name? He doesn't know, he only met Joe in a bar and had a few drinks with him. Where does Joe live? In Louisville, Kentucky, the man thinks. So, of course, we can't find Joe. Well, in ninety-nine cases Joe is someone dreamed up to manufacture an alibi, but in the one case Joe really exists, and the guy goes to prison because we can't find Joe. If the prosecution needed to find Joe, the Louisville police would help, and maybe they would find Joe. At least they'd have a chance. But the wretch can't even put up bond to get out of jail so he could try to find Joe himself. So what chance does he have?"

"Spoken like an old defense lawyer," I said.

"Spoken like a humanitarian," said Betty, rejecting my levity about the matter.

"Well, what do you suggest we do about it?" I asked.

"Set up a state-financed system of public defense for the indigent," said Bob. "Provide the truly indigent defendant with what he gets now, which is a lawyer, and also provide him with a minimum of assistance to that lawyer in the way of investigatory services, plus an allowance of money to pay transportation for witnesses and such expenses."

"Is that practical?" I asked.

"No," replied Bob frankly. "But can we afford to do less?"

The waitress arrived to take our orders. I was glad she did because I do not ordinarily enjoy such serious conversation with my lunch. I have found, to my annoyance, that young people tend to become serious and reserved in the company of people who are ninety-two years old. I could not complain that this pair was reserved, but serious they certainly were. I know that if I had not been with them the conversation would have been light and witty and iconoclastic and suggestive. Do they think that because I am ninety-two years old I want to sit around and debate jurisprudence and theology? I do not have that appearance. I am a wizened old man, slight of stature as I have always been, with wispy white hair, but I smile and laugh, and I would like to think, as a conceit of my old age, that my bleary old eyes twinkle.

164

We teach them to respect their elders. Well, now that I am *the* elder in town I have assured myself of what I long suspected: there is not a damn thing about old age to be respectful about. I wish they would treat me like a young man. I wish they would talk as they talk among themselves. I am not a stranger among the people who now own the earth, or at least I do not want to be. I suppose in their sight I am an alien among them, but they need not remind me of it daily.

While we had our lunch we talked about various criminal cases which have excited public interest in the country in the past few years. We talked about the Sheppard case, and, like most young lawyers, Bob was firmly convinced of the defendant's innocence in that case. We talked about a California case, the name of which I do not remember, in which a doctor and his pretty young mistress were finally convicted of murder by their third jury after two hung juries. The point of interest for us in that case lay in the question of how many times a case can be retried before due process forbids trying it again. It is interesting to observe what a difference in emphasis there is when a professional discusses a subject and when a layman discusses it. Mark Twain, I believe it was, wrote a humorous paragraph on a beautiful girl as the physician must see her—rather, as the physician must read her; and he commented how tragic it must be not to be able to appreciate her merely as a beauty instead of as a bundle of symptoms. It is humorous exaggeration, but as with all good humor it bears within it a treasure of philosophy. As a lawyer and judge I see the criminal trial from a viewpoint entirely different from that of the layman. I see it like this:

In every trial the community as well as the accused is put to a test. The layman finds his interest in the test of the accused, in the proof of innocence or guilt, in the verdict and the judgment. I find my interest in the test of the community. The measure of the community's commitment to liberty must be found in its treatment of the criminals it has reason to hate. Due process of law is easy to give to the little thief who stole a few dollars, but can we give it as well to the despicable villain who is manifestly guilty of a crime that shocks us all? If our commitment to human rights is total, we can. If we cannot, we become a police state. In every trial, we the people are tested, and our conduct as a people and as a government places us somewhere on a scale of values, somewhere between liberty and tyranny. That is what I look for. How do *we* test, we the people, we the community? Do we demonstrate our commitment to freedom, or do we allow our emotion about the crime to drag us away from that commitment? That is the importance of a trial. If we mistakenly acquit some dangerous criminals and loose them to sin again, that is too bad, but we will survive it; but if we destroy our liberty to win the battle against crime and find ourselves living in a nice, sterile, crime-free police state, we will not survive.

I think we listen too much to professional policemen. I do not mean to belittle them—they do much good. But we must recognize the mentality of the professional policemen and consider that mentality in weighing their words. It is important to prevent crime and to punish it when it occurs, but it is more important to be a free people. The professional policeman, single-minded in the pursuit of his goal, is apt to be impatient of the civil liberties which hinder him, and his attitude rubs off on public opinion. Well-meaning people snipe destructively at basic and vital features of our system of liberties and never realize the harm they do. I do not much fear the attack of a totalitarian foreign power on our liberties, because we will recognize that attack and defend ourselves effectively. I do not much fear domestic totalitarian philosophies for the same reason; sooner or later we will recognize them and fight back. But I much fear the respectable and benevolent citizen who thinks he knows what he is doing but ignorantly leads his fellow citizens to sacrifice some cherished right because he does not understand its importance and thinks it may be safely given away to achieve some other purpose he does understand.

For example, if the Communist Party of America were to suggest that the government forbid all criticism of the Soviet Union in the interest of better foreign relations, we would remind those zealots that we Americans have freedom of speech and will say what we like about the Soviet Union or anyone else, and we would reject with indignation any such suggestion. But, when the league of mothers and fathers comes along and demands censorship of books and magazines to protect their children against pornography, how do we respond then? That is not so easy to handle. Few have the courage to scout the demand. Yet the one suggestion is as much an attack on freedom of speech as the other. On principle there is no difference between them. We can defend the Constitution against the first group with no embarrassment, but we may lose our battle with the second. The idea is too attractive. Surely, the argument runs, we can sacrifice a little freedom of speech to such an end. So we sacrifice a little, whittle away a little here and a little there; we damage the structure, and we lose more and more freedom.

I am a libertarian. I regard human liberty above all other values. In the enthusiasms of my youth I often fell into the trap I have described, but for fifty years at least I have been a fanatic about liberty. Most of the phrases which so well express the concepts contained in the Bill of Rights have become meaningless clichés, bandied about as much by the enemies of freedom as by its friends, and it is ironic that in America in the twentieth century a man can sound a little silly talking about these things.

But, as the comedian says, I digress. . . .

While we ate our lunch the conversation continued, and I enjoyed it in spite of feeling ancient in the company of Bob Day and his wife. In time Bob began to carry the conversation. He tends to enjoy his own dissertations, but I must admit he has much to talk about, and he does not bore me. There is little about which he will hesitate to express an opinion, and he has confidence in his opinions, even in those he holds only a day or two. One thing he told interested me considerably. It relates to what I have just been discussing. He said that a friend of his was teaching American government to college classes. This instructor administered to his classes an examination in which he asked a question concerning a man who climbed up on a soap box to make a speech. The man was arrested when he defied a policeman's order to get down and be quiet. The question was more complex than my simple statement of it and contained several other facets, but the point was that the students were to analyze the situation and write an essay as to whether freedom of speech was violated. Approximately one-third of the class wrote, in effect, that the man was properly arrested and should be convicted because citizens must do what policemen tell them to!

When we finished our lunch we went back to the courthouse.

VIII

WE RETURNED to the courthouse a few minutes before the trial was to resume. I went to my office, intending to answer three letters which had come for me that morning. People say my office is out of character. They seem to think a man my age ought to have an old roll-top desk, brass cuspidors, and old-style files with the papers tied up in bundles with red ribbon. I once had an office like that, but the county commissioners were always good enough to provide me with new equipment as I needed it, so my office furniture is quite modern and ordinary. I do have in files and on shelves the massive accumulation of papers and books a man inevitably acquires and keeps over a long tenure of office. I shall not sort it out. I mean to evade that responsibility, and leave the task to the executor of my estate. It will be a puzzling job for him. I was an executor several times before I became a judge, and since I retired I have acted as appraiser of estates on a number of occasions. It is sad when you reach my age and know that someone will be sorting and appraising your property before long. As an appraiser I have walked through the deserted rooms of houses and have seen the treasures of a lifetime, now left behind by the treasurer. To the appraisers, those treasures are junk. We marvel that anyone could have allowed such junk to accumulate; that is, we marvel until we return to our own homes and glance over the things we keep. We understand only when we imagine ourselves for the moment to be impersonal appraisers looking over our own property. It will be so in my office. The appraisers of my estate will marvel at the things I have preserved, but I have a reason—or once had anyway—for keeping every book and paper I have. If my office is furnished in a contemporary style, it at least has the clutter of an old man's room, and in that respect it satisfies the anticipation of visitors.

I had a visitor, for a moment. Judge Henry Kemp came in and told me that he had received an anonymous telephone call during the noon recess. A woman wanted to tell him that she knew Ruth Gibson was guilty. I asked Henry what he had said to her.

"I told her," he said, "that she was in contempt of court. I told her I would put her in the county jail if I found out who she was. Then she hung up."

"I used to get an anonymous letter now and then," I said.

"I've had three about this case. If there is anything I can't stand," he said sharply, "it's a dirty, cowardly anonymous letter or call. If they have something to say but don't have enough conviction to identify themselves when they say it, I feel they ought to be horsewhipped."

"What do your anonymous letters say?" I asked him.

"Well, let me get you one and show you," he said, and before I could protest he hurried out of the room. In a moment he returned and handed me the three letters.

I examined them. Each was written by a different hand. Two were on little sheets of stationery, and one was written on a sheet of notebook paper folded over and stapled and with the address and stamp on the folded sheet. All were postmarked Alexandria.

The one on the folded sheet of notebook paper read: "Dear Judge, If you believe anything said by Doc Russell you must be a fool. He's a liar. How else do you think he's screwed every girl in town? By promising to marry them. The cops got it in for Ruth Gibson and Roger Louis. Doc Russell stold that stuff himself, and everybody knows it. Justice must be done."

Another read: "Every decent Christian in town knows all about that Gibson whore. If you think we are going to vote for you to be judge again if you let her get away with all she's done, you have another think coming. Your friend Roger Louis is nothing but a drunken bum and a liar and a thief. I am not the only one who thinks so. All my friends and neighbors say the same thing and also that you will not be judge another term if you don't send them both where they belong. Remember, this town is going to be watching you."

The third said: "Alexandria, Sodom, Gomorrah. All the same. Louis, Gibson, Russell. All the same. Sinners sit in jujmant on sinners. God knows. I know. Jesus known. The Blood of Jesus Christ Cleanseth All from Sin. What diff. one sinner more or less in Alexandria? All town drunk, gamble, sex. Only hope in Jesus Christ. I sine myself, Friend."

When I had read the letters and given them back, the judge placed them in his coat pocket, and together we went into the courtroom.

Everyone was in place. Everything was the same. I noticed that Ruth Gibson had put on a little lipstick, as Bob had told her to do, and had combed out her hair. Se did not look as grim as before. Roger Louis glanced at her when she came in, then quickly turned his head away, as if the sight of her were distasteful, or as if he had been told to promote the impression that he no longer had any interest in her.

MacInroth called the first witness for the defense—a man in clean, freshly pressed work clothes. He said he was a foreman at the Caesar's Creek Plant of Gardner Metals Corporation and Roger Louis's immediate superior. His name was James Folke.

"Are you acquainted with the defendant, Roger Louis?"

"Yes."

"Would you say you are well acquainted with him?"

"Pretty well."

"Are you generally acquainted with people who know Roger Louis and with people he knows?"

"Yes."

"On the basis of that acquaintanceship, are you able to form an opinion of the reputation of Roger Louis for honesty and for being a law-abiding citizen?"

"Yes."

"Would you say his reputation for honesty, among the people he knows and who know him, is good or bad?"

"Good."

It sounds a little ridiculous, but that is the formula for introducing reputation into evidence. Folke was a character witness. This little chain of questions was of major significance in the trial. It meant that the defense was placing Louis's character in issue, and of course if the defense elects to try to prove that a defendant's reputation and character are good, then the prosecution can try to prove them bad. This is an option the defense enjoys. Unless the defense places reputation and character in issue, the prosecution cannot attack them; they are regarded as irrelevant. But once the defense opens the door, the prosecution also can pass through it.

"And what about his reputation for being a law-abiding citizen?"

"That is good too," the witness said dutifully.

"Have you been foreman over Roger Louis ever since he went to work in your plant?"

"Yes."

"Is he a steady worker?"

"Yes."

"Does a good job?"

"I got no complaints."

"Did Roger Louis ever try to borrow money from you?"

"No."

"To your knowledge does he try to borrow money from the other men at the plant?"

"One of the boys lent him five dollars once that I remember. That's the only time I know of."

"Do you know whether the five dollars was promptly repaid?"

"I suppose it was. I never heard anything said about it."

"All right. Thank you. That's all."

"Mr. Folke," said Joe Baumgardner, "when you said that Roger Louis has a good reputation for honesty and for being a law-abiding citizen, did you know that he wrote a bad check in Peter Showalter's gasoline station last winter?"

"No."

"Thank you. That's all."

The defense next called one William Taylor, who worked in the plant and also said that he was a personal friend of Louis.

"Has Roger Louis visited in your home, and have you visited in his?"

"Yes, sir."

"Are you acquainted with a group of people who know Roger Louis and whom he knows?"

"Yes."

"On the basis of your acquaintanceship with people who know him and who are known by him, are you able to state an opinion as to his reputation among his circle of acquaintances for being honest and a law-abiding citizen?"

"Yes, he—"

"Is that reputation good or bad?"

"Good."

"Thank you. That's all."

Joe Baumgardner stood up and waved the witness, who had risen to leave, back to his seat. "Mr. Taylor, when you testified that Roger Louis has a good reputation for honesty and for being a law-abiding citizen, did you know that he had written a bad check in Peter Showalter's gasoline station last winter?"

"Yes, I heard about that."

"But in spite of the fact that you know he defrauded Showalter by cashing a bad check in his station, you are still willing to testify that he has a good reputation for honesty?"

"I think that could happen to anybody."

"What could happen to anybody?"

"He could write a bad check."

"Is it your understanding of the facts that Louis merely overdrew his account?"

"I guess so."

"Did you know that at the time when he wrote a check for two hundred dollars he did not have even one hundred dollars on deposit, and in fact at no time during that month or the month before did he have even one hundred dollars on deposit?"

The witness, a blond young man of some twenty-five years, who was dressed in a checkered sport coat and a shiny broad blue necktie, sat looking at Baumgardner for about a minute, and then at the end of this embarrassing silence, he asked, "Am I supposed to answer?"

"Well," said Joe Baumgardner in a mock tone of patience, "we rather thought you would. The question is, when you say you think Louis simply made a mistake and overdrew his account, did you know his check was written for more than twice as much money as he had had in the bank for several weeks?"

"I didn't know how much money he had in the bank."

"You didn't know that when he wrote a check for two hundred dollars, he had in his account—" Joe Baumgardner looked for the figure on his yellow legal pad. "Twenty-four dollars and twenty-four cents. You didn't know that?"

"No, I don't keep track of other people's bank accounts."

"Well, let me ask you this then: If you knew as a fact that a person wrote a check for two hundred dollars on his account and cashed it when he must have known he didn't have that much in the bank, would that leave you thinking that that person was honest?"

"Objection," said MacInroth, but he could not stop the witness, who answered anyway.

"That's the chance a guy who cashes checks takes."

"I see," said Joe Baumgardner, and he made a little bow toward the jury. Several jurors were laughing. "Let's talk about something else, then, Mr. Taylor. You are married, are you not?"

"Yes."

"And your wife's name is—?"

"Anne."

"You have two children?"

"We got a third one coming."

"Roger Louis has often been to parties at your house?"

"Yes."

"Was your wife at those parties?"

"Yes."

"Does everyone drink at those parties?"

"Some."

"Did Roger Louis ever get drunk at your house?"

"Objection!" said MacInroth. "That is irrelevant. The defendant's reputation for sobriety is not in issue."

"But his reputation for being a law-abiding citizen is," said Joe Baumgardner. "If he gets drunk and does antisocial things, that is not law-abiding."

"It will be admitted," ruled the judge.

"The question is, did Roger Louis ever get drunk at your house?"

"A little I guess, sometimes," answered Taylor with a shrug.

"And did he cause a problem for your wife?"

"No."

"Well, did your wife ever threaten to leave you if you did not keep Roger Louis out of the house?"

"Objection."

"It will go to show an act much less than law-abiding," said the prosecuting attorney.

"Go on."

"Answer the question, did she or didn't she?"

"Well, she got excited about him one time," said Taylor, trying by his tone and manner to minimize.

"What caused her to get excited?"

"Objection."

"Overruled."

The witness followed the exchange of words with his eyes, from MacInroth to the judge and then back to Baumgardner, who was waiting for an answer. With a resigned motion of his hands, Taylor said, "Well, she thought he was trying to put the make on her one time."

"Objection."

"Overruled."

"And by 'trying to put the make on her' what do you mean?"

"Well, he got kind of smart with her one time."

"What did he do, specifically?"

"The defense preserves its objection."

"It is noted and overruled."

"What did he do?" pressed Joe Baumgardner.

"Well, he tried to kiss her."

"Is that all?"

"That's about all."

"You say it's 'about all.' Let me remind you, young man, that you are under oath here to tell the truth and the whole truth. Now, you have testified that your wife threatened to leave you if you let Roger Louis in the house again. What did he do to her that made her say that?"

"Objection."

"Overruled."

Taylor waited a moment, as if expecting some further interruption, and then he said, "Well, he tried to pull her dress up."

"He tried. And did he succeed?"

"She wouldn't let him."

"No, I suppose not. But did he succeed anyway?"

"Some, he did."

"You say he did have some success. By the way, Mr. Taylor, where were you when this was happening?"

"I was there."

"Did it occur at one of your parties?"

"Yes."

"Who all were present?"

"A bunch of guys."

"Any other women besides your wife?"

"No."

"In other words, you were having the fellows in for a drinking party?"

"To play cards."

"Okay. And you did some drinking too?"

"Yes."

"What did you drink?"

"Beer."

"Had Roger Louis been drinking beer when this happened?"

"Yes."

"Had you been drinking beer?"

"Yes, some."

"And your wife?"

"She'd had a couple."

"Was she pregnant at the time?"

"Yes, a couple of months."

"Where was your wife when Roger Louis pulled her skirt up?"

"She was bringing him a beer, and he pulled her down in his lap."

"Then he pulled up her skirt?"

"Yes."

"What, if anything, did he say to her?"

"He told her I'd lost her to him in the card game."

"Had you?"

"Hell, no."

"He was just kidding her?"

"Sure."

"Did she laugh?"

"At first she did."

"But then he pulled her dress up. You were about to tell us a little while ago how far up he pulled it. How far, Mr. Taylor?"

Taylor looked down and said, "Pretty far, I guess."

"Did he expose her panties?"

"Objection," said MacInroth. "If the court please, I think this has gone too far already. This frolicking at a drinking party between a half-drunk Roger Louis and a half-drunk Mrs. Taylor is entirely irrelevant and highly prejudicial."

"Mr. Baumgardner," said Judge Kemp. "You said you were going to reveal some antisocial conduct. I must say, what you have developed so far is not done in polite society, but it is not the sort of thing the court expected you were going to develop when I let you pursue this line of questioning. We cannot go on."

"Your Honor," said Joe Baumgardner, "I apologize for taking so much time getting to the point. It is, you will admit, a little difficult to get the witness to admit the facts. What I am getting at is no frolic. It will only take one or two further questions."

"I will permit one or two further questions then, but I hope you are getting to something relevant."

"I still object," said MacInroth, sitting down.

"It will be noted. Continue."

"Mr. Taylor, did Roger Louis pull your wife's skirt above her waist?"

Taylor hesitated for a second and then said, "Yes, he did."

"Did he then attempt to pull off her panties?"

"He grabbed at them."

"Did he pull them down?"

"Partly."

"Exposing her crotch?"

"Partly."

"What did he say to her?"

"Objection."

"Overruled."

"He asked her to go in the bedroom with him."

"And what did she say?"

"She didn't say nothing. She just screamed and tried to hit him."

"And what prevented her from getting away from him?"

"He had a hold of her."

"And what finally stopped him?"

"One of the other fellows at the table reached over and hit him."

"Hard?"

"Hard enough to break his front tooth." Taylor had ceased to resist the questions. Apparently the recollection of the incident had stirred in him some forgotten anger, and his attitude toward Roger Louis was not so friendly as it had been when he took the stand.

"And what were you doing, Mr. Taylor, while Roger Louis was trying to strip your wife?"

"It all happened pretty quick, and I didn't know he was serious about it."

"You didn't do anything?"

"Well, no."

"Did you throw him out of the house then?"

"He was mad about his tooth, and he ran out the door."

"And as a consequence of this incident, your wife told you she would leave you if you ever let Roger Louis come to your house again?"

"Yes, that's what she said."

"And did you thereafter let him come to your house?"

"Well, not for a long time. She won't stay in the place when he's there."

"Now, if the court please," said MacInroth, rising to his feet. "This recitation has been admitted into the record over our objection. This jury has unquestionably been hopelessly prejudiced against my client by this irrelevant testimony. I regret the necessity, but I move a mistrial."

"Your motion is overruled," said the judge immediately.

"Preserving our objection to continuing at all, we then move that all this testimony be stricken from the record and that the jury be instructed to disregard it."

"Overruled," said the court again, just as quickly. "You put your client's character in evidence, and you will have to stand for hearing derogatory evidence, just as the prosecution will have to sit and let you introduce evidence of his good qualities."

"If the court please, that is not the law," said MacInroth.

"I think it is, Mr. MacInroth," the judge said.

MacInroth turned to Day and whispered something in his ear. Roger Louis, through all this, sat with the same shadowy expression on his face, looking at the surface of the table most of the time. I could not see Ruth Gibson's face; her back was toward me; but people told me later that she had seemed amused by Taylor's testimony.

Almost as an afterthought, as if he had forgotten he was there, MacInroth looked up at Taylor and told him he was dismissed.

Bob Day spoke and called another witness. This was a fat, gray-haired woman I had seen around town but did not know. She was obese and short of breath.

"State your full name please," said Bob.

"Mrs. Woodrow Cummins," said she in a slow and precise manner which was obviously not her natural manner of speaking. She was impressed with the dignity of the occasion.

"Your address?"

"Eight-four-two Bridge Street, Alexandria, Ohio."

"You are a widow, Mrs. Cummins?"

"Yes, sir."

"Are you acquainted with the defendant Ruth Gibson?"

"Yes, sir."

"How long have you know her?"

"About two years," said Mrs. Cummins, still separating each

word from every other and speaking slowly. While she spoke, she gestured with her hands, moving them forward and back and from side to side, and she tipped her head to one angle and another. This habit gave further emphasis to her words. At the end of every answer she had to draw her head back to its natural position.

"In what circumstances do you know her?"

"I rent her a room in my home."

"And have you done so for two years?"

"Yes, sir."

"During that period of time, have you become acquainted with Ruth Gibson and with a group of people she knows and who know her?"

"Yes, sir."

"On the basis of that acquaintanceship with a group of her acquaintances are you able to state an opinion as to her reputation for honesty and for being a law-abiding citizen?"

"Yes, sir."

"Is her reputation good, or bad?"

"It is good. Very good."

"Do you provide her with meals?"

"No, but she often eats with me. I like to have her, and I ask her."

"Does Ruth do some of your grocery shopping for you?"

"Yes, until they put her in jail she did most of that for me."

"Did you give her the money to do that for you?"

"Yes. I have given her various sums of money to do shopping for me. Not only groceries but other things too. I don't get around too well. I'm too fat."

"Did you ever have reason to suspect that she might be keeping any of your money?"

"No, never. I have given her endorsed checks to cash for me, and I have given her large amounts of cash. She always brought me back whatever change I had coming."

"Did you pay her anything for doing your shopping for you, by reducing her rent or otherwise?"

"No, she just did it to be nice to me. I offered her something for doing it, but she would always say she was glad to do it."

"Did she help you with the house?"

"Yes, she often did my dishes for me, and sometimes she did the clothes or the ironing. While we were watching TV in the living room at night she would set up the ironing board and iron her clothes and mine too."

"Did she go to church?"

"Yes, the first Sunday she was with me I asked her if she wanted to go to church with me, and she did, and since then she has gone almost every Sunday—that is, until they put her in jail."

"Thank you, Mrs. Cummins."

Joe Baumgardner continued the questioning.

"Mrs. Cummins, you say Ruth did this and that during the evenings when she was home with you. Was she home often in the evenings?"

"No, she worked evenings mostly."

"At what time did she get off work, do you know?"

"Ten o'clock usually, I think."

"Would she then arrive home at ten-thirty or eleven?"

"Yes, if she came right home she would."

"Did she usually come right home?"

"Sometimes she did, and sometimes she went out after work."

"Did she go out after work often?"

"Pretty often."

"And what time would she get in when she went out after work?"

"I don't know. It would be after I went to bed."

"What time did you customarily go to bed?"

"After I watched the Jack Paar show or a movie. Maybe one o'clock."

"So she would come in after one o'clock?"

"Yes, sir."

"What time would she get up in the morning?"

"Ten or eleven mostly."

"Did you know who she went out with?"

"Sometimes she told me. Sometimes she didn't say."

"Did she tell you she was going out with men?"

"Surely. Wouldn't a girl her age be going out with boys?"

"Now, you have testified that you believe her reputation for honesty is good. How about her reputation for chastity?"

"Objection!"

181

"If the court please," said Baumgardner, "the question of the defendant's morals is in issue. The question of her conduct with Paul Russell puts that in issue."

"I will allow the witness to answer this question," said the judge. "I do not intend to allow a wild excursion, however."

"How about her reputation for chastity?" said Baumgardner, turning back to the witness.

"Her reputation is good in every way," said Mrs. Cummins positively.

"Well, when you say that, what if anything do you know about her conduct with these boys she went out with?"

"I don't know anything about that."

"If she conducted herself badly, you don't know of it?"

"No."

"Your testimony that her reputation for chastity is good is based on your assumption that she has not been guilty of any sexual misconduct?"

"I don't think she ever did anything like that."

"Okay. That's all."

Mrs. Cummins lifted herself from the chair and stepped down from the witness stand. Instead of heading for the door, however, she walked over to the defense table and took Ruth Gibson by the hand, and with her other hand she patted her on the head. In a low voice she said something I could not hear. Before anyone could object, she had turned away and moved toward the door. Ruth Gibson put her head down on the table and began to cry. She was not loud about it. To the contrary, no one heard her, and if she had not shaken gently and if she had not raised her head a few minutes later and needed a handkerchief to wipe her eyes, no one would have known she was crying.

Bob Day called another witness. This was Harvey Perkins, the minister of the church to which Mrs. Cummins said she went with Ruth Gibson. He said his church was called The Holy Evangelical Church. It is a fringe sect—on the fringe of sanity, in my opinion. They hold forth in a frame building on the edge of town and shout and holler as they pray and sing. It is not a respectable church, but it has a considerable congregation. Like all churches of its flavor, it appeals to the least literate classes in the community. The trouble with the traditional or older churches is that they become stuffy. The common people don't feel welcome or comfortable in them, and their religion is so subtle and abstruse these people don't understand what is being said in church. They want to hear about hell-fire and damnation and about how Jesus can save them from it. They want to hear how God loves them. They want these simple ideas dinned into their ears every Sunday, without complication and without social philosophy thrown in on the side. They don't get it in the old churches anymore, so they form these little churches to provide what they want in the way of religion.

"Reverend," said Bob Day, using a form of address to which the minister was not accustomed, though Bob did not know it, "are you acquainted with the defendant Ruth Gibson?"

"Yes, sir, I am," said the minister crisply.

"Is she a member of the congregation of your church?"

"Yes, sir, she is."

"Did she attend your church regularly?"

"Yes, sir, she did, up till the time when she was put in jail."

"Have you visited with her while she has been in jail?"

"Yes, sir, I have."

"At her request?"

"Yes, sir, at her request."

"How often do you see her?"

"I try to go every Sunday afternoon to see her and pray with her in the jail."

"Are you acquainted, Reverend, with a group of people who are acquainted with Ruth Gibson, who know her and whom she knows?"

"Yes, sir, I am."

"On the basis of that acquaintanceship are you able to form an opinion as to her reputation for being honest and a law-abiding citizen?"

"Yes, sir, I am."

"What is that reputation, good or bad?"

"I would say her reputation is very good. I hold her to be a good and devout Christian."

"Thank you. That is all."

Joe Baumgardner stood up and faced the witness. To cross-examine a minister is always a bit touchy. In the minds of some people a minister, no matter of what church, ought to be exempt from criticism or challenge. Mr. Perkins was a little white-haired ruddy man, a fierce-looking man when he preached, I am told. He had simply no end of assurance; he was a man for whom all questions are settled. Since he has no doubt in his mind about anything of consequence he can afford a degree of confidence which would be entirely beyond the rest of us.

"Sir," said Joe Baumgardner carefully, "you say you are satisfied that Ruth Gibson has a good reputation and is a devout, practicing Christian. I wonder on what quantity of information you base that opinion. Did you ever see her between Sundays?"

"Not very often, no, I didn't," the minister said.

"When you called at Mrs. Cummins's house, was Ruth at home ordinarily?"

"Not ordinarily, no, sir. I usually called during the afternoon when she would be at work."

"Did you ever see her at her work?"

"They serve liquor in the place where she works, sir," said the minister.

"So you would never go there?"

"No, sir, I would not."

"So you saw Ruth Gibson on Sundays only, when she was in church, for the most part. Right?"

"Yes, sir, that is right."

"On those Sundays, did you talk to her or did you just see her in the congregation?"

"Except on a few occasions when she and Mrs. Cummins stayed to talk after the service, I only saw her in the congregation."

"Have you discussed Ruth Gibson with other members of your congregation? Let me restate that question. Before the robbery of DeWitt's Jewelry Store, was Ruth Gibson often the subject of conversation between you and other members of your congregation?"

"No, sir, she was not."

"Did you, in fact, ever talk about her at all?"

184

"No, sir, not that I recall."

"Your estimate of her reputation and character, then, is based entirely on the fact that you saw her in your congregation on many Sundays?"

"No, sir, not entirely. I have had many conversations with her since she has been a prisoner. I have formed my opinion principally from those talks."

"During those conversations has she talked to you about the robbery of DeWitt's store?"

"Yes, sir, she has."

"Did she, by any chance, admit that she committed the crime?"

"Objection!" said Bob Day. "Any conversation she had with her minister is privileged. He cannot be asked to testify about that."

"Reverend Perkins," asked the court, "is confession to your minister any part of the discipline or doctrine of your church?"

"My congregation is taught to confide in their pastor," said the minister.

"Is that a sacrament of confession?"

"No, sir, it is not."

Bob Day, who had been whispering with MacInroth, ended the discussion by saying suddenly, "I withdraw my objection. He may answer."

"I withdraw the question," said Joe Baumgardner quickly, before the witness could speak. "And I have no further questions."

"I have," said Bob Day. "I want the answer to the question the prosecutor withdrew, Reverend. Did she confess to you that she committed the crime?"

"No, sir, she did not. She repeatedly denied it."

"Thank you. That is all."

It had, of course, suddenly occurred to Bob Day that he could not object to the question the prosecutor had asked without creating the impression that Ruth Gibson had in fact confessed the crime to her minister. His objection had been a sort of conditioned reaction to the question, but as soon as he paused to think about it he wanted the question answered. By that time Baumgardner did not want it answered. He would rather leave the implication as it was. So Day had had to pick it up on redirect.

"Call William Reitlinger," said Bob Day then.

Quentin went out and brought back Billy Reitlinger. He owns a restaurant right off the courthouse square. Reitlinger's, usually called Billy's, is a restaurant and bar for working-class people. Not many doctors or lawyers eat there, and they never do when their wives are with them. I do not mean to suggest that the place is at all gamey. It is not that. It is just that Billy serves a heavy fried meal with lots of fried potatoes, served to most customers with a fishbowl of draught beer. He does a big bar business, selling besides the beer a considerable quantity of wine and much whisky. He does not, on the other hand, sell many Martinis. His customers come in for a big beer after work and then come back in the evening for a little whisky and conversation. He hires lots of buxom country girls as waitresses, and, though one of them gets a pinch occasionally from some exuberant drinker, the place is nevertheless respectable, and Billy allows no one to get ostentatiously drunk or noisy in his place.

Personally, Billy Reitlinger is a happy innkeeper. He presides over his bar all day, hears all the stories and repeats them, drinks a little of his own beer. He has been there since prohibition was repealed, and during the prohibition years he had a roadhouse where the thirsty traveler could order beer or whisky if Billy trusted him. He trusted me, thank God. Now he is bald, short, bespectacled. To see him in the courtroom dressed in his dark suit and without his white apron seemed strange. He spoke to many of the crowd, including several of the jurors, as he crossed the front of the courtroom to take his seat on the stand.

"State your full name, please," said Bob Day.

"William T. Reitlinger," said Billy.

"Your address?"

"Route Four, Alexandria."

"And you are the owner of Reitlinger's Restaurant, commonly known as Billy's?"

"Yes, I am."

"Do you know the defendant Ruth Gibson?"

"Yes, very well."

"In what connection do you know her?"

"She works for me, or did up to the time she was arrested."

"For how long did she work for you?"

"It would be a little over three years."

"Do you know her pretty well then?"

"Oh, sure."

"Do you know the people with whom she generally associates, who know her and whom she knows?"

"Yes."

"On the basis of that acquaintanceship are you able to form an opinion as to her reputation for honesty and for being a law-abiding citizen?"

"Yes, her reputation is for being a good, hard-working kid. Nobody can say any different."

"Would you be willing to hire her back if she is acquitted?"

"I've told Ruth," said Billy affirmatively, "that she has a job waiting for her whenever she wants it, whether she gets out of jail in a few days, or even if she has to serve a sentence in prison. I'll never believe she's guilty of anything, and I'll take her back any time."

"We'll have to object," said Joe Baumgardner.

The judge shook his head at Billy, who had looked up quizzically, and said, "You will have to confine your answers to the questions asked." Then he spoke to the jury and said, "The jury will disregard the witness's statement of opinion as to the guilt or innocence of the accused."

"Did she handle money in the course of her work for you?" Bob Day asked.

"Yes, she did. I never had a cent missing. Sometimes I gave her the sack of money to take to the bank for me. She would take several hundred dollars, maybe over a thousand once or twice, and go to the bank with it for me. I was never afraid to trust her."

"What were her hours?"

"Well, they varied. Mostly, though, she came in about one or two in the afternoon and worked until nine or ten. She would work longer hours if I asked her to for any reason. Never any complaint."

"I take it you would say she did a good job?"

"The best. Best waitress I ever had."

"Did your customers try to date her?"

"Sure, all the time. But she wouldn't go out with them. Except once in a while when she knew somebody pretty well, she would."

"You've heard her turn men down?"

"Sure. Lots of times."

"What about Paul Russell?"

"I heard her turn him down several times before she finally agreed to go out with him. Which was a mistake."

"Paul Russell has testified that Ruth Gibson agreed to go out with him the first time he asked her. Is it your testimony that she refused him several times before she agreed to go out with him?"

"Doc Russell is a liar," said Billy Reitlinger. "I heard him ask her for dates two or three times and heard her say no every time until finally she said she would go out with him on the third or fourth time he asked her."

"Did she ever tell you why she quit going out with Russell?"

"Objection," said Joe Baumgardner. "That would be hearsay."

"Sustained."

"That's all. Thank you."

Joe Baumgardner looked up at the witness and smiled and said, "You like her pretty well, don't you, Billy?"

"I sure do," Billy said.

"Yes. I have no further questions."

While Billy Reitlinger proceeded along the front of the jury box and toward the door, John MacInroth called the next witness, Richard Berenger, the proprietor of Ted's Men's Shop. I should explain that it has been many years since there was a Ted in Ted's, and then the name did not refer to the owner's first name but to his last name, Tedder. He was called Ted, though, and his store, originally Tedder's, became Ted's irretrievably and he was compelled to accept it. Tedder has been dead since 1925; Berenger's father bought the store from the estate. Dick Berenger has run it since about four or five years ago when old Richard Berenger retired. Dick is about fifty, tall and very thin, thin-faced, with a long chin and a pointed nose. He reminds me of the stringy male who appeared in silhouette on the Toulouse-Lautrec poster for the Moulin Rouge.

"State your full name, please," said MacInroth.

"Richard John Berenger."

"Your address?"

"Twenty-three hundred Elm Terrace, Alexandria."

"Your business?"

"I am the proprietor of Ted's Men's Shop."

"Is that next door to DeWitt's Jewelry Store?"

"Yes, it is."

"Were you in your store on the morning of May twenty, the day on which DeWitt's was allegedly robbed?"

"Yes."

"At what time did you arrive in the store?"

"Oh, about eight-thirty to eight-forty-five."

"And were you in the store continuously from that time until the time when Paul Russell came in and told you he had been robbed?"

"Yes, I was there all the time."

"At what time did Russell come in and announce the alleged robbery?"

"At about nine. I would say it was nearly exactly nine, because we were just opening the door."

"At the time he came in, what were you doing?"

"I was turning on the lights."

"And where in the store are the switches which turn on the lights?"

"Behind the counter where the cash register is. And that is about midway between the street door and the back of the store."

"From there could you see the street in front of your store?"

"Yes."

"Would you have a clear view?"

"I could see out the glass door and out the show windows. Of course, in the windows there were mannequins with clothes on, so they would obstruct the view somewhat."

"And what had you been doing immediately before you turned on the lights?"

"Opening the cash register."

"And before that?"

"Switching on the lights in the showcases. Each one has its own little switch."

"Did you at any time, either before Paul Russell came in or

after, observe a green 1950 Chevrolet parked in front of your store?"

"No, I did not."

"When Russell came in did you run to the front of the store and look out to see the robber?"

"Well, I didn't run, but I looked, and I went to the front and looked up and down the street."

"And did you see the car?"

"No."

"Did you see any car of that description?"

"No."

"Did you see, or had you seen, any man in a blue jacket or any man who looked like the defendant Roger Louis?"

"No."

"Had you observed any automobile with a girl sitting in it, a girl like the defendant Ruth Gibson?"

"No."

"Do you recall if, when you went and looked out, the traffic was heavy on the street in front of your store?"

"There were a few cars moving and a few parked. Traffic was not heavy."

"Were there pedestrians on the street?"

"Yes, a few."

"All right. Thank you."

Joe Baumgardner rose and went to stand before the jury box. "Dick, it is entirely possible, is it not, that the automobile could have been parked in front of your store for the three or four minutes the robbery might have taken without your noticing it?"

"I suppose that is possible," said the witness, emphasizing the word possible to convey clearly the impression he thought it not at all likely.

"When you were working around your cash register and turning on the lights in your cases, your attention would be fixed on them for several minutes at a time, would it not?"

"Yes."

"Now, when you went out and looked up and down the street, what kind of a car were you looking for?"

"For a green 1950 Chevy."

"In other words, you are saying that Paul Russell told you the make and model and color of the car immediately when he came running in your back door, before you went out to look?"

"Well, no; he told me that later, after we called the police."

"So when you went out to look, you weren't looking for any particular kind of car, were you?"

"I guess that would be right, yes."

"How long would you judge it would take Paul Russell to run out the back door of DeWitt's, up the alley, and in the back door of your place? Do you have any idea?"

"I wouldn't be able to put it in seconds. The doors are heavy fire doors; they have to be pushed hard. My back door wasn't locked. He came right in."

"In the time it would take him to run out the back door of DeWitt's, up the alley, and in your back door, and in the time after that it would take you to get out the front of your place and look up and down the street, do you think a car that had been parked in front of your store with the motor running could have driven up the street and around the corner if the light was green?"

"I couldn't say. Maybe he could. Maybe he couldn't."

"Okay. That's all. Thank you."

"I have one further question," said MacInroth. "Dick, in testifying that you did not see an automobile parked in front of your store at about the time the robbery is supposed to have taken place, did you mean to say you did not see a green 1950 Chevrolet parked there, or did you mean to say you saw the two parking stalls in front of your store empty?"

"All I saw, whenever I looked out, were two empty parking stalls."

"That is all. Thank you. No, wait. One thing more. Was anyone in the store with you at the time?"

"A couple of the boys who work for me."

"Where were they?"

"In the stock room."

"So they couldn't have seen anything?"

"No."

"That then *is* all. And thanks again."

"Mr. MacInroth," said the judge, "have you any objection to our recessing for fifteen minutes at this time?"

"No, your Honor."

"The jury is admonished again not to discuss the case or form any opinion until all the evidence has been heard. The court will stand in recess for fifteen minutes."

IX

AFTER THE RECESS, MacInroth called David MacKay to testify. MacKay is a young man, in his twenties, a big man, more than six feet tall, weighing more than two hundred pounds. He has thick blond hair, which he allows to grow rather long, and on this day in court he was dressed in a light blue suit slightly too small for him, undoubtedly because he was gaining weight. He relaxed on the witness chair and seemed to challenge the lawyers to begin to ask their questions.

"State your full name, please," said MacInroth.

"David John MacKay."

"Your address?"

"Route Five, Alexandria."

"Where do you work?"

"Down at the Caesar Creek plant," said MacKay in a relaxed, conversational tone.

"Do you work in the same department as the defendant Roger Louis?"

"No."

"Are you acquainted with the defendant Roger Louis?"

"Yes."

"How long have you known him?"

"Him and me went to high school together. I've known him ever since."

"Does he visit in your home and you in his?"

"Yes."

"Now I would like to direct your attention to Friday, May nineteenth, which, to refresh your recollection, is the day before a robbery allegedly took place at the DeWitt Jewelry Store. Do you remember that day?"

"Yes, sir." The witness casually crossed his legs.

"Did you work on that day?"

"Yes."

"Did Roger Louis work that day?"

"Yes."

"Did the two of you get off work at the same time?"

"Yes," said MacKay. He nodded with each yes.

"What time was that?"

"Four o'clock."

"Did you meet when you got off work?"

"Yes."

"For any particular reason?"

"Yes, sir. Me and him was going out on a fishing trip that night, and we got together as soon as we got off work."

"Where did you meet him?"

"In the parking lot at the plant."

"Was anyone else with you then?"

"No, sir, not at that time."

"What did you do?"

"Well, we talked about whose car we was going to take with us fishing, and we said we'd take his so's I could leave mine at home for my wife, and then we drove to my place so I could leave my car."

"Then what did you do?"

"Well, we put my fishing tackle in his car and then we went to pick up some beer and groceries to take with us."

"Where did you go for the beer and groceries?"

"We went to Dizzie's store down on River Street."

"And then where did you go?"

"Well, we stopped by his place so's he could pick up some more stuff, his sleeping bag and some stuff, and then we drove out to the place where we go to fish."

"Where was that?"

"Out on Greenwater Creek, up County Road Seven and out Greenwater Creek."

"How far from Alexandria is that?"

"About twenty mile," said MacKay without hesitation. The exchange of questions and answers proceeded rapidly as MacKay responded confidently and so quickly he almost cut off MacInroth's last word.

"What time did you arrive there?"

"I expect it was about six."

"Was anyone else there?"

"Yes."

"Who was that?"

"Dean Drayer, another friend of ours."

"Was he there to fish with you?"

"Yes."

"Was anyone else there that night?"

"No."

"Now, how long did you stay there?"

"All night and up to about noon the next day. Roger, he left about ten or ten-thirty, and I went back home in Dean's car."

Here, then, was the alibi. They were trying to prove that Roger Louis was fishing when the robbery took place. Bob Day had promised this in his opening statement, and it shouldn't have surprised anyone. Yet it came out so casually that people in the courtroom were stirred to comment to those sitting with them, to ask, I suppose, "what did he say? what did he say?"

"What did you do there all night?" MacInroth went on.

"We fished a lot, and we ate and drank beer, and we went in swimming in the creek."

"Did you catch anything?"

"I caught a cold," said the witness, evidently pleased with his humor.

"Any fish?"

"Only some mudcats and a carp or two."

"Did you get any sleep?"

"A little, early in the morning."

"Did you have with you a watch or any other way to tell the time?"

"Yes, I had my wrist watch on."

At this point MacInroth paused before asking his next question. He wanted to gain attention by slowing down the hurried exchange of question and answer.

"At nine o'clock in the morning of Saturday, May twenty, was Roger Louis with you?" asked MacInroth in a large voice.

"Yes, sir, he was," the witness said affirmatively. He nodded as he spoke, as if confirming his testimony.

Now Roger Louis looked around the courtroom, and for the first time his face bore a smile. It was a smile of genuine amusement. He was having a moment of triumph.

"What time did Roger Louis leave you?"

"It was ten or ten-thirty."

"Did he say why he was leaving?"

"He said he had a date with his girl."

"What girl was that?"

"Ruth Gibson."

"When he left, did you ask him to make a telephone call for you?"

"Yes."

"Who did you ask him to call?"

"I asked him to call my wife and tell her I was coming home pretty soon."

"Why did you want him to do that?"

"Because we had said we was going to stay out till Sunday, but we weren't getting any fish to amount to anything, so we decided to give it up."

"Returning to the time when Roger Louis left you, how do you know what time it was?"

"Well, I know what time it is most of the time. I wear a watch," MacKay explained, again thinking he was being witty.

"Did you take particular notice of the time it was when he left you?"

"Well, yes, because I wanted him to call my wife."

"And you are certain it was not before ten?"

"It might have been a few minutes before, but it couldn't have been earlier than a quarter till ten," said MacKay, very carefully.

"And at nine o'clock he was with you?"

"Yes."

"All right. Thank you."

Joe Baumgardner remained seated, and as he asked questions of this witness he also made notes. "You say," he began, "that you spent the whole night out there on the bank of the creek?"

"That's right," said the witness, sitting up straighter. He knew the difference between friendly direct examination and searching cross-examination.

"How much beer did you take with you?"

"About three cases, counting what Dean brought."

"How much did you have left to take home?"

"I don't remember," said MacKay, still quick with his answers.

"Well, did you drink a great deal of it?"

"Pretty much of it, yes," the witness said.

"And did you then get drunk on it?"

"Pretty much, I suppose," the witness agreed with a nod.

"So drunk that you went swimming in the creek in weather much too cold for that sort of thing?"

"Yes, I expect that's why we went in," MacKay said, grinning.

"And caught cold?" asked Baumgardner, serious and not responsive to the grin of the witness.

"Yes, sir."

"So this was a pretty drunken party you had?"

"I guess you'd have to call it that."

"Was that the first time you had done that?"

"The first time this year."

"You had gone out fishing and drinking and swimming that way before, then?"

"Yes, sir."

"You say you arrived there at six o'clock?"

"Yes, sir."

"What time did you catch your first fish?" asked Baumgardner slowly; he too finding it necessary to cut down MacKay's pace.

"I don't remember that," MacKay said immediately.

"What time was it when you went in swimming?"

"I don't remember what time that was."

"Well, it was after dark, wasn't it?"

"Oh, yes."

"Was it after midnight?"

"I expect it was. I don't know for sure."

"What time was it when you slept?"

"Early in the morning."

"What time?" Baumgardner insisted.

"I'm not sure."

"What time did you wake up?"

"It was light, but what time it was I don't know."

"You don't know what time you woke up?"

"No," said MacKay calmly.

"Did you build a fire?"

"No, sir."

"Eat breakfast?"

"Well, yes, we had some bread and lunch meat and stuff. We ate that."

"What time was that, when you ate?"

"I don't remember what time that was."

"You do remember, however, that at nine o'clock Roger Louis was with you?"

"Yes, sir," MacKay replied innocently, nodding.

"You didn't pay any attention to the time all night, but at nine o'clock when a robbery was taking place in town, that time you took careful note of, is that right?"

"Objection," said MacInroth.

"The question *is* argumentive," said the judge.

"Did you take off your watch when you went in the water?"

"Yes, sir."

"Did you wear anything at all when you went in the water?"

"No, sir," said the witness with a broad grin.

"Now you say you caught some fish," said Baumgardner carefully and quietly. "Who caught what?"

Baumgardner plainly thought the witness was lying. He thought Roger Louis had procured this witness and Dean Drayer, the third member of the fishing party MacKay was describing, to come to court and lie for him. He knew that people who make up a story will arrange to agree on all the essential points, but they cannot anticipate and agree on their answers to all the questions about little details. Baumgardner would ask questions about every small detail of the fishing trip. He would note the answers. Then he would ask the same questions of Drayer, and if Drayer's answers were not the same the jury would know the story was a fabrication.

The witness considered the question about the fish for a moment, and then he said, "I'm not real sure who did catch what fish. I got a mudcat, a big one, and Roger caught a carp, but how many each man got I couldn't say."

The principal difficulty with this technique of cross-examination is that a witness of average intelligence will immediately recognize it. If the witness is lying he can defend himself against this kind of cross-examination by exhibiting a selective memory, by remembering the essentials on which he and his collaborators have agreed, and by professing not to recall the nonessential details. The cross-examiner, of course, will comment on the selective memory. It suggests the lie. But the witness can respond that he naturally remembers important things and forgets minor details, and the jury can believe this, for such has been their own experience and the common experience of mankind. When a witness exhibits a selective memory, you really cannot know whether he is lying or not.

"What brand of beer did you have?" Baumgardner asked. Now he was willing to go fast if the witness wanted speed.

"Burger."

"Was it all Burger?"

"To the best of my recollection."

"Did you drink any more when you got up in the morning?"

"Yes."

"How did you keep it cold?"

"We laid the bottles in the water along the edge of the creek."

"You didn't take any ice?"

"No."

"What was Roger Louis wearing when he left you?"

"I don't remember."

"Well, did he have on a coat and tie?"

"No."

"A blue jacket?"

"No."

"White shirt?"

"I expect so, maybe."

"Blue jeans?"

"Yes, I guess so."

"And he left you at what time?"

"About ten o'clock."

"All right. That's all."

As the witness stepped down, Roger Louis looked up at him and grinned, as if to say he was well satisfied with the way his friend had met his cross-examination. When MacKay was out of the room and before the next witness was called, MacInroth turned and said something to Roger Louis, and Louis did not smile or grin again during the trial. Louis has the habit of leering when he smiles, and MacInroth did not want the jury to see it again.

"Call Dean Drayer."

Drayer impressed me mostly by the vigorous way he chewed gum throughout his testimony. He was a dark-haired, slim, tall young man, dressed in a dark blue suit and tan shoes. He told MacInroth that he lived in Alexandria in a boardinghouse and was a produce man in a supermarket.

"Are you acquainted with the defendant Roger Louis?"

"Yes, sir," said Drayer. He had a way of speaking his answer and then staring at the lawyer with an anticipatory expression that invited another question.

"How long have you known him?"

"Three or four years, as long as I've lived here."

"Calling your attention to Friday, May nineteenth of this year, which was the day before DeWitt's Jewelry Store was allegedly robbed, did you see Roger Louis on that day?"

"Yes, sir," said Drayer, chewing his gum vigorously.

"Where and when did you see him?"

"Well, him and me and Dave MacKay was supposed to go

fishing out at Greenwater Creek. I went out there and seen him and Dave first come along about six in the evening."

"How long did you stay there?"

"I stayed there all night and till about noon the next day."

"Was Roger Louis with you all that time?"

"He was until about ten o'clock the next morning."

"At nine o'clock on the morning of May twenty where was Roger Louis?" MacInroth asked in a big, significant tone.

"Out there on Greenwater Creek with us," the witness said emphatically with two quick nods.

"And what time did he leave there?"

"About ten o'clock."

"How far is it from the place where you were all night back to Alexandria?"

"Eighteen mile. I checked it."

"Thank you. You may cross-examine."

Baumgardner, of course, turned back to the first page of the notes he had taken during the cross-examination of MacKay.

"How much beer did you take out to Greenwater Creek with you, Mr. Drayer?" he asked.

The question plainly surprised the witness, but he looked down and chewed his gum contemplatively for only a few seconds before he replied, "Well, as best as I can recall, I took out a case I picked up at the store before I started out."

"How much did MacKay and Louis bring?"

"I don't know. Maybe more than I did. We had a lot of beer. At least a case apiece, I expect."

"How much of it did you drink?"

"Most of it, I expect."

"Did you get drunk?"

"No," said Drayer quickly.

"Did the others?"

"No."

"Mr. Drayer, did you go in swimming in the creek?"

"Yes, sir," the witness said with some enthusiasm. The thought seemed to amuse him.

"It was pretty cold for swimming, wasn't it?"

"Oh, not too cold," he said with a shrug.

"Was it the first time you went in swimming this year?"

"Yes."

"Did you catch cold?"

"No."

"Did MacKay?"

"I don't know."

"Did MacKay get drunk?"

"No."

"He says he did. Do you still testify that he didn't?"

"I can't help what he says."

Baumgardner turned away from his yellow legal pad of notes and took from his file a sheet of white paper with typing on it. "Mr. Drayer," he asked, "how long have you lived in Alexandria?"

"About three and a half years," said Drayer after a moment's hesitation.

"Where did you live before that?"

"Charleston, West Virginia."

"Ever have any trouble with the police?"

"Not especially."

"Police never gave you any difficulty?"

"No."

"Where were you during the year 1956?"

"What?"

"Where were you during the year 1956?"

"I was in the penitentiary at Moundsville," said Drayer, quite blandly, without the slightest sign of embarrassment.

"Moundsville, West Virginia?"

"Yes."

"Serving a sentence for forgery?"

"Yes."

"Was that your first conviction for forgery?"

"No."

"Was it your second?"

"Yes."

"Is this correct?" Baumgardner asked, making up his question from the paper in his hand and speaking with slow precision. "You were convicted of forgery in 1953 at Charleston and placed on probation. You were convicted a second time in 1955 and served two and a half years in the penitentiary. Is that correct?"

"I pleaded guilty," Drayer objected.

"How's that?"

"I pleaded guilty. I wasn't convicted," Drayer explained in a manner plainly meant to imply an important distinction.

"But you did do it each time?"

"Yes."

"And you did serve two and a half years?"

"Yes."

"Don't you call that trouble with the police?" Baumgardner said, laughing.

"No," said the witness immediately. "It wasn't no trouble with the police. They caught me, I admitted it, and they sent me up."

It was more his manner than his words, but everyone in the courtroom had to laugh at this. Even MacInroth smiled.

"Anyway, when you moved here you had just been released?"

"Yes."

"What time did you say you arrived at Greenwater Creek?"

"About six o'clock."

"I thought it was the other two who got there at six."

"Well, I was just a little bit ahead of them. There wasn't no point in sitting out there all by myself," said Drayer in a patient, explanatory tone.

"What time was it when you caught your first fish?"

"I never caught any."

"What time was the first one caught by any of you?"

"I think Dave got one the first hour we was there," the witness said slowly and thoughtfully.

"What kind of fish was that?"

"Mudcat. All we got was mudcats."

"No bass?" asked Baumgardner.

"No."

"No suckers?"

"No."

"No carp?"

"No," said Drayer. "Just mudcats."

"How many fish all told did you catch?"

"Didn't get none myself, but I guess Roger got a mudcat, and Dave got a couple."

"Big ones?"

"Roger's was."

"What time did he catch it?"

"Late. I don't know what time, but late."

"What time was it when you went in the water?"

"Late too."

"What time?"

"Oh, after midnight, I expect," Drayer speculated.

"What time was it when you got some sleep?"

"Didn't get none."

"None of you?"

"Well, I guess Roger got some," Drayer corrected himself slowly. "He had a sleeping bag. He said he had to get up and go see his girl in the morning."

"But neither you nor MacKay slept at all?"

"No, we were up all night, he and I."

"What time did Roger Louis get up?"

"It was daylight."

"Did you build a fire and cook any food?"

"No."

"Did you eat in the morning?"

"In the morning and all night, whenever the spirit moved," Drayer said with a grin.

"What did you have to eat?"

"Bread, meat, potato chips, cheese, cookies, and stuff like that I got from the store."

"Did Roger Louis and MacKay bring any groceries?"

"No, just beer. I brought all the groceries."

"When you went in swimming did you wear anything?"

"No," said Drayer, laughing.

"What brand of beer did you have?"

"Two or three kinds, I guess. Burger, Iron City."

"Did you have any ice to cool it?"

"No, we drank it warm."

"Put any in the creek to cool it?"

"I guess Dave did do that with some of it."

"What was Roger Louis wearing when he left you?"

"Blue jeans and a white shirt," said the witness quickly.

"What time was that again?"

"About ten."

"And when did you and MacKay leave?"

"Around noon."

"Do you remember any talk about a telephone call?"

"Yes, Roger was supposed to call Dave's wife and tell her we was coming home instead of staying over till Sunday."

"Why did you and MacKay stay after Louis left?"

"We just wasn't ready to leave yet," Drayer shrugged.

"Why?"

"Well, we wanted to fish a little more, for one thing."

"That's for one thing. What other reasons?" Baumgardner demanded.

"I don't know. No particular reasons I guess."

"All right. That's all."

What good was Drayer? It would be difficult to say. On the one hand, he certainly was not an impressive witness, and his criminal record suggested the truth was not in him. On the other, he was a jolly fellow, quite bland about his crimes, and everyone laughed at him. There are, after all, honest criminals who commit their crimes defiantly and admit them openly. They steal because they want to steal, but they don't lie about it. The distinction is not too subtle for any jury to understand. Whether our jury would make the distinction, I could not guess.

The next witness called by the defense was Eileen MacKay, Mrs. David MacKay, a sloppy-looking pregnant woman, who testified that Roger Louis had indeed called her to report that her husband would be home on Saturday instead of Sunday, that he had called about ten-thirty, and that he said he was calling from a gasoline station called Sherry's Fork Station. Little time was spent on her.

The defense now asked for a ten-minute recess, which was granted.

"That didn't amount to much, did it?" Bill Mullen asked of me after Judge Kemp had stopped momentarily at my place on his way out and had then gone on.

"What didn't?"

"The alibi. I don't think the jury was impressed with those witnesses."

"Well, that's hard to say," I remember telling him. "It wasn't dramatically presented, but it didn't break down on cross-examination either."

"Oh, I don't know. He caught them up on some differences in stories."

"Not too much. Maybe enough to impress the jury. That's hard to say. It gives Baumgardner something to argue about anyway."

Quentin Strickland, the bailiff, had joined us during my last comment, and he now chipped in and said, "Those fellows are lying, Judge. That's as clear as the nose on your face."

"How do you know they are, Quentin?" asked Bill Mullen. He was baiting Quentin a little. A lot of people do. They like to hear him talk.

"Well," said Quentin, "one of them says they got drunk, and the other says they didn't; one says they only drank Burger beer, and the other says Burger and Iron City; one says they all brought groceries, and the other says he brought 'em all; one says they got some sleep, and the other says they stayed up all night. The fact is they weren't none of them out there that night. They was all home in bed, and Roger Louis was plotting his robbery. Then take that Drayer, a convicted crook. You wouldn't believe anything he said, would you?"

"I don't know about that last point," said Mullen. "If I were Roger Louis and getting somebody to lie for me, I surely wouldn't get an ex-convict and forger. It almost seems to go to prove they *were* out there, or else Roger would have gotten himself a better witness."

"Maybe that's all he *could* get," argued Quentin. "He isn't loaded down with friends, from what I hear."

"He certainly wasn't overloaded with good character witnesses," said Mullen.

"That's a fact." Quentin laughed. "When Joe Baumgardner got that fellow to admit how Roger tried to pull his wife's pants off, I thought I'd die."

"So did some of the jury," Mullen said.

206

I wondered how Joe found out about that.

"Some of Roger's friends aren't too enthusiastic about him, I imagine," said Mullen. "Maybe the wife herself called Joe."

"Yeah, maybe," laughed Quentin.

"Anyway, Judge," said Mullen more seriously, "to get back to our original point, don't you think the alibi was a little weak? That's all the defense there is, and it didn't seem to amount to much alongside of what the prosecutor had."

"I don't know. I am glad I've been a judge and not a juror," I said.

X

J‌OHN MACINROTH CALLED the defendant Roger Louis to testify in his own behalf, during the afternoon of the second day of the trial.

Louis got up from his seat at the defense table, unwillingly, you could see, as though he were leaving a refuge and venturing forth into danger, which in a sense he was. He shuffled forward, stooped in posture, until he reached the witness stand where the clerk was waiting to administer the oath. Other witnesses had been sworn outside, but MacInroth wanted his client sworn before the jury, so the jury could see him take his oath on the Bible.

"You do solemnly swear that the testimony you are about to give in the cause in hearing will be the truth, the whole truth, and nothing but the truth as you shall answer to God?" recited the clerk.

"I do." Louis took the stand. Still dressed in his checkered sport coat and his red satin necktie, he hunched forward in the chair and clasped his hands in his lap.

"State your full name," said MacInroth.

"Roger Larimer Louis," mumbled Louis.

"Speak up a little, so the jury can hear you," said MacInroth. "Where do you live, Roger?"

"Out in the country here, outside of town. What they call the old river road."

"How old are you, Roger?"

"Twenty-seven."

"Now, Roger, I'm going to ask you one question just to get it out of the way, and to have a clear understanding at the outset. Did you rob DeWitt's Jewelry Store?"

MacInroth put his question positively and with as much drama as he could, but his defendant merely shook his head and said, "No."

"Did you, on May 20, 1961, at about the hour of nine o'clock in the morning, enter DeWitt's Jewelry Store with a pistol and rob the clerk Paul Russell of money and jewelry?" asked MacInroth, trying again to be emphatic.

Everyone in the courtroom sat up stiffly and stared at Roger Louis. He looked down at the floor, shook his head again, a little sadly, I thought, and simply said, "No."

"Very well," said MacInroth. "Now let's talk about the events of May nineteenth and May twentieth. In the first place, start with the time you got off work on May nineteenth and tell the jury what happened and where you went."

"Well," said Louis, "we got off work at four, and me and Dave—"

"Now, Roger," MacInroth interrupted, "it is going to be necessary for you to talk louder. Talk to the jury, not to me; I know what happened; they don't." MacInroth left his seat and walked over to the jury box to stand. With some witnesses an attorney has to go and stand by the jury box; otherwise they will talk to him and not to the jury—that, or else jerk their heads back and forth in a comic fashion as they try to talk to both.

"We got off work at four o'clock," said Louis more loudly and with some embarrassment and irritation.

"All right. Then what happened?"

"I met Dave MacKay in the parking lot because we was going out fishin' that night."

"Go on." MacInroth had to urge his witness.

"Well, we went to his house so he could leave his car. He got in my car, and we went to Dizzie's to get some beer to take with us. Then we went to my house to get some stuff of mine. Then we went out to Greenwater Creek."

"What time did you arrive there?"

"About six o'clock."

"How long did you stay at Greenwater Creek?"

"Till about ten the next morning."

"Did you ever leave during that time, that is, between six in the evening of May nineteenth and ten in the morning on May twentieth?"

"No."

"What did you do all night?"

"We put out our lines and fished. And we drank beer and ate, and we went in swimming."

"Did you sleep any?"

"I did, some. Not much."

Louis kept his head down, but he looked up and spoke in the direction of his attorney, and the jury could hear him. His voice was low and hesitating, even though he was answering questions he had certainly heard before, and even though the manner in which he spoke also suggested some memorizing of the answers. He kept his hands clasped in his lap, moving only his thumbs as he uncrossed and crossed them again, first right over left and then left over right; and this movement he made repeatedly and mechanically, time after time.

"Did you drink much beer?"

"I guess I did, pretty much."

"Get drunk?"

"Yeah, pretty much," Louis said.

"Who was with you at Greenwater Creek?"

"Dave MacKay and Dean Drayer," responded Louis, looking up at his lawyer as if he were surprised at the question, as if commenting that his lawyer well knew his companions.

"What time did you leave?"

"About ten."

"You mean ten in the morning?"

"Yeah, in the morning," Louis said, nodding.

"May twentieth?"

"Yeah."

"Why did you leave at that time?"

"Well, I'd told Ruth I'd pick her up Saturday morning. I was going to bring her back out to Greenwater Creek, but the fellows and me decided we wouldn't stay any more."

"The original plan was to take her out to your fishing camp?"

"Yeah."

"Why did you change your plan?"

"Well, we was all wet and soggy and cold out there, and we wasn't catching anything, and it was too cold to swim much. So there wasn't no point in staying."

"When you refer to Ruth, you mean Ruth Gibson, don't you?"

"Yeah."

"All right. You left about ten. Then where did you go?" MacInroth had to lead and prompt Louis. Louis would begin an answer, and it would sound as though he were going to go right on and tell his story, but in a moment he would fumble to a halt and MacInroth would have to start him again.

"Well, I went to get Ruth, like I said."

"Where did you get her?"

"Where she was living, at Mrs. Cummins's place," Louis said. His manner suggested that these questions were obvious and that he should not have to answer them.

"What time did you pick her up?"

"Pretty near eleven."

"Did you call Mrs. MacKay before or after you picked up Ruth Gibson?"

"Before."

"Okay, you picked up Ruth. Then where did you go?"

"Well, I told her we couldn't go out to Greenwater Creek. So we talked some about where to go, and we made up our minds to go up to the old house on the ridge."

"On Shambles Ridge, you mean?" MacInroth prompted.

"Yeah."

"All right. Why did you go there?"

"So we could be alone," said Louis with a larger voice, almost defiant. "It was someplace we could go alone."

"You had been there with her before?"

"Yeah."

"What time was it when you got there?"

"Eleven-thirty. Quarter to twelve."

"What did you do there?"

"We fooled around."

"By that do you mean you had sexual intercourse?" asked Mac-Inroth, and the people in the courtroom became visibly more attentive.

"Yeah."

Neither of the defendants reacted visibly to the public revelation of this fact. They were prepared for it. Louis answered the question without hesitation, and Ruth Gibson just kept looking steadily at him as she had at most of the witnesses.

"What were you doing when the sheriff came?"

"The same thing."

"Well, describe what happened."

"Well, we was in bed, and we heard this car coming," Louis said, betraying some impatience. "There aren't many cars up there on that road, so we noticed it. Then we heard the car stop up the road a little piece. There ain't no other place they could be going if they stop up there, so we figured they was coming up to the house. So we got up and put our clothes on and looked out the window, and pretty soon we seen the sheriff and the deputy sneaking up the road toward the house. So we took off."

Louis recited his story flatly, showing no emotion. He told it as a tale he had told too many times before, as if he forgot that the jury was hearing it for the first time.

"Why did you run?"

"Because they were coming after us, and we didn't want to get arrested. We were scared."

"What did you think they wanted to arrest you for?"

"We figured it was because we were up there doing what we were doing," said Louis.

"Do you mean you thought they had come to arrest you because you had been having sexual intercourse?"

"Yeah."

"All right. So you ran. Then what happened?"

"Well, like the sheriff said, when we got to the top of the hill, Ruth said she was tired and couldn't run no more, so she laid down in the bushes, and I run on down the other side."

"Then where did you go?"

"Well, I run down the valley for a ways. Then I cut up over the next hill and down the ridge some and pretty soon come out on another road."

"Was that Pine Tree Road?"

"That's what they tell me. I didn't know the name of it."

"Then what did you do?"

"Well, I started walking along that road. I was sorta lost, but I figured that road would come out somewhere and I would go back and get my car. A couple of cars came along, and I tried to hitch a ride, but they wouldn't stop. Then the sheriff's car came along."

"And they arrested you."

"Yeah."

"Tell us about your arrest."

MacInroth's questions were short and precise and put quietly to reduce his own role in the drama. It was not like cross-examination, not an exchange between attorney and witness. He wanted Louis to tell his story with as little prompting as possible. He wanted the jury's attention not on himself but on the witness.

"Well," said Louis, "they just drove up beside me, and the fellow driving asked me who I was. I told him, and he said I'd have to go with them. So I got in the car."

"Did they put handcuffs on you?"

"After I got in the car and we got started, the little fellow, Handschumacher, told me I'd have to put out my hands, and he put them on me."

"What, if anything, did you say about Ruth Gibson while you were in the car?"

"I said she sure had got me in a mess. I still thought they had got me for what I did to her."

"Objection," said Joe Baumgardner. "We will move that the last statement of the witness be stricken as self-serving."

"Sustained," said the judge. "The jury will disregard the explanation as to why he said what he said."

"What, if anything, did you say about Paul Russell?"

"I never said nothing about Paul Russell," said Louis aggressively.

"Did you mention the name Paul Russell?"

"No," said Louis quickly.

"Roger, have you ever been in DeWitt's Jewelry Store?"

"No."

"Never?"

"Never."

"Do you know Paul Russell?"

"No."

"I mean to ask, were you acquainted with him before May twentieth?"

"I didn't know him from Adam," said Louis contemptuously.

"Did Ruth Gibson ever, at any time since you have known her, say anything to you about robbing DeWitt's Jewelry Store?"

"No."

"Did she ever say anything about Paul Russell?"

"Yeah, she said she used to go with him."

"Did she ever say anything about his cooperating in a robbery or anything like that?"

"No."

"Never?"

"Never."

"All right. You may cross-examine," said MacInroth to Baumgardner.

Baumgardner looked up at the witness appraisingly. Roger Louis slowly turned toward him and stared back balefully, and for a moment they faced each other like the antagonists they were. Baumgardner was calm and professional, but Louis took the prosecution as a personal assault against him by the prosecuting attorney. His resentment was evident in every line of his hunched body and his dark face. If it is possible to look like a criminal, Roger Louis looked like one at that moment. The jury seemed to see it, too.

Baumgardner looked away from Louis and down to his notes. He selected a question, and he asked, "Did you say it was your plan originally to stay out on Greenwater Creek until Sunday?"

"Yeah," Louis answered.

"Well, then was Ruth expecting you when you came to her place on Saturday morning?"

"Yeah."

"How is that, if you planned to stay until Sunday?"

"I was always supposed to come back and get her Saturday morning."

"Do you mean it was part of the plan for you to come back to town and get her on Saturday morning?"

"Yeah."

"Well, what were you going to do with her in your fishing camp?"

"Don't know what you mean," said Louis shortly.

"Well, does she like to fish and drink beer and swim in the frigid creek with you and your two men friends?"

"I don't know."

"Was she going to stay all night with you Saturday night?"

"I don't know. We hadn't said."

"Why didn't you take her with you Friday night?"

"She had to work Friday night."

"Did she have to work Saturday night?"

"No, Saturday was her day off that week."

"It was your plan, then, for her to spend most of Saturday out on the creek bank, and probably Saturday night too?"

"I guess so."

"With you three men?"

"Yes."

"Neither of them had a girl with them?"

"No."

"You say you had sexual intercourse with her up in the house on Shambles Ridge?" asked Baumgardner.

"Yeah."

215

"Did you expect to do the same out on the creek bank?"

"No."

"She was just going fishing with you?"

"Yeah."

"Just going to sit out on the creek bank all day with you and your two friends?" asked Baumgardner in a soft, amused voice.

"Yeah."

"That was the way she was going to spend her day off?"

"Yeah."

"Where was her landlady when you came to the house to take her out?"

"I don't know. I didn't see her," Louis said, leaning back in his chair and drawing a deep, disgusted breath.

"Did you see anyone around when you went to the house to pick up Ruth?"

"No."

"No one saw you?"

"Not that I know of."

"Why was it that you ran from the sheriff?"

"We was scared."

"Of what?"

"Of being arrested," Louis exhaled, conveying his annoyance at being asked these questions again.

"Why did you think they were coming to arrest you?"

"Because of what we were doing in the house."

"Well, now Roger, really, how would they know about that?"

"I don't know. We never stopped to think about that," said Louis, almost angry. Baumgardner could have led Louis into a show of temper by making him go over the same point several times. Some witnesses can't stand that.

Carrying his yellow legal pad, Joe Baumgardner walked up to the witness stand. "You want this jury to believe that you thought the sheriff and a deputy were coming to arrest you for having sexual intercourse with Ruth Gibson?" he asked.

"Yeah," replied Roger Louis flatly.

"How old is Ruth, do you know?"

"Twenty-one or two, I guess."

216

"Did you ever hear of anyone being arrested for having intercourse with a woman who is of age?"

"I don't know."

"How do you suppose the sheriff and his deputy knew that was what you were doing there anyway?"

"I don't know," said Louis, closing his eyes.

"If you heard him coming and got up and dressed, how could he know what you had been doing even when he got there?"

"I don't know," said Louis, separating the words.

"It's pretty ridiculous, isn't it, Roger?"

Louis paused for a moment and then broke into a grin and said, "It sure is." There was laughter in the courtroom, and Roger Louis had scored a point with the jury. The sudden grin which broke the sullen expression he had worn for two days put a gloss of humanity on the wooden character the jury was studying. His ingenuous, almost good-natured admission that part of his story sounded ridiculous lent it an air of truth that unyielding adherence to it could not have done. Baumgardner had a good point. The story Louis was telling was simply unbelievable. Louis, however, with his little grin had momentarily obscured the point a bit. In a trial, no lawyer can plan or prepare for every possibility.

Baumgardner understood what had happened and tried to bring the emphasis back to his point. "Besides, your car was sitting down at the road. They could identify you by that, and you really couldn't escape by running up the hill, now could you?"

"No," said Louis, his grin gone and his body returned to its customary hunched position.

"So why did you run?"

"We was scared."

"In fact, you were in a panic, weren't you?"

"Yeah," said Louis with a trace of enthusiasm, glad to hear the suggestion.

"But what caused you to panic, Roger? This ridiculous idea that the sheriff had come to get you for having sex relations with this girl could not cause such a panic, now could it?"

"Well, it did," insisted Louis.

"Well, it is ridiculous, you admit?"

"Yeah."

"But if you had just committed an armed robbery and thought you had escaped clean, and here comes the sheriff sneaking up toward the place where you had gone, that would reasonably cause panic, wouldn't it?"

Bob Day spoke up. "Now that he's made his point I don't suppose there's much profit in objecting to the argumentive question, but we do object and ask that the court instruct the prosecuting attorney to confine his argument to that point in the trial where argument is in order."

"Yes, Mr. Baumgardner," said the judge. "The point is well taken."

"Excuse me, your Honor," said Joe Baumgardner smoothly. "Roger, where did you think you were running to?"

"Didn't know," said Louis, shaking his head. "We was just scared and run."

"Just scared and run," repeated Baumgardner. "How long a term of imprisonment did you fancy went with having had sexual fun and games with this girl?"

"Well, they might have thought we broke in the house," suggested Louis.

"Oh? Now that's a new point. When did you think of that?" Baumgardner asked with a smile.

"Just now," replied Louis innocently.

"But that was not what you thought at the time, am I right? At the time you ran away because you thought they had come to get you for having sexual intercourse with Ruth?"

"Yeah."

"How many times did you have intercourse with her while you were there in that house?"

"Two or three times."

Baumgardner was laying much emphasis on the fact that the two defendants had been having sexual relations. He had cause to suspect that at least some of the jurors would not believe anything said by a pair who were sexually promiscuous. Besides, it reinforced Paul Russell's charge that Ruth Gibson was morally loose and had used her body to tempt him.

"Was that the first occasion on which you had had intercourse with her?"

"Objection," said MacInroth. "I don't think it is necessary to go into that. It is irrelevant and prejudicial."

"The objection will be sustained," said Judge Kemp.

"Well then, let's talk about something else," said Baumgardner. "Do you deny that you wrote a bad check in Peter Showalter's service station?"

"Objection," said MacInroth. "Irrelevant and prejudicial."

"If the court please," said Baumgardner, "it goes to the credibility of the witness."

To bring evidence that a defendant has committed other crimes is ordinarily irrelevant and prejudicial, as MacInroth suggested; but since the defendant had elected to testify as a witness in his defense, he could be asked about an act of his which would tend to prove him dishonest. In other words, as a witness, his credibility became a proper subject of inquiry, and the implication of course was that anyone who would write a bad check was basically dishonest and would lie from the witness chair. Realizing the implication, the judge overruled the objection.

"Do you deny that you wrote a bad check?" Baumgardner repeated.

"No," said Louis. Baumgardner would have hoped that Louis would try to argue about it.

"You needed money pretty badly, didn't you?"

"Yeah," Louis said readily, not seeing any point in the question.

"In fact, needing money is chronic with you, isn't it?"

"What?"

"You always need money, don't you?" said Baumgardner, putting it simply.

"Sure, who doesn't?" mumbled Louis, looking down.

"Well, you wouldn't contend that it is common for young men to have their wages repeatedly attached by creditors, would you?"

"I don't know."

"You had been told shortly prior to the robbery, had you not, that you would lose your job if you didn't avoid any more attachments of your wages?"

"Yeah."

"So you needed money unusually badly, didn't you?"

"Not bad enough to steal it," said Louis clearly and positively, looking squarely at Baumgardner.

"Well, writing a bad check is stealing, isn't it?"

"Not like taking it with a gun, it isn't," Louis said more loudly.

"I agree," said Baumgardner. "But you do not deny, do you, that you needed money very badly about the time of the robbery?"

"Do I deny it?" Louis asked in a puzzled tone.

"Yes, do you deny it?"

"No."

"Do you drink a good deal, Roger?" asked the prosecutor conversationally.

"I drink some."

"What do you drink?"

"Different things."

"Beer?"

"Yeah."

"Whisky?"

"Yeah."

"Wine?"

"Yeah."

"Gin?"

"No, I don't like gin." He looked up and grinned shyly, and again the crowd laughed heartily, even Baumgardner.

"Well, Roger," said Baumgardner when the courtroom quieted, "you do some pretty wild things when you get to drinking, don't you?"

"I don't know," said Louis. It was a denial, when he put it that way.

"Well, trying to pull your friend's wife's panties off was not nice, was it?" asked Baumgardner briefly.

"No." Louis said after a moment's hesitation.

"Object and move that the jury be instructed to disregard the question and the answer," said MacInroth, without much confidence in the ruling he would get. The judge overruled him.

"Do you drive your car when you are drinking?"

"Objection."

"Sustained."

"Well, have you ever been convicted of driving under the influence of alcohol?"

"Yes, once."

"When was that?"

"Three or four years ago."

"Spend your three days in jail?"

"Yeah."

"You do own a green 1950 Chevrolet?"

"Yeah."

Louis spoke in a flat mumble again. He didn't like these questions.

"Do you own a blue jacket, one that zips up the front?"

"No."

"Do you own a pistol?"

"No."

"Now just to get this straight, when you ran from the sheriff, you did so because you thought he somehow knew you were having sexual intercourse with Ruth Gibson, and you thought he wanted to arrest you for that. Is that right?"

"That's right."

"Very well. That's all."

MacInroth and Day rose and walked up to the bench, where Baumgardner joined them, and a moment later the judge recessed the trial until nine the next morning. It was still rather early in the afternoon.

The cross-examination of Roger Louis must have seemed weak to the devotees of television drama. It was not exciting. Nothing much was brought out. Baumgardner had been able to emphasize the implausibility of the defense's story that the two defendants ran from the sheriff because they thought he had come to arrest them for immorality. Other than that he had not accomplished much. He had spent most of his time attacking the credibility of Roger Louis as a witness. That was all he could do. That was the nature of the case. The stories of the principal witnesses were simply and basically contradictory, and the case was resolving itself into a question of taking one group's word against the word of the opposing group of witnesses. In those circumstances, the credibility of witnesses becomes vital.

I could not say, having heard the testimony and cross-examination of Roger Louis, that he had accomplished much for himself, but neither had he hurt his case. In fact, the impression was growing, not only in my mind but in the minds of many of those watching the trial, that Roger Louis was something of a neutral quantity in the case and that Ruth Gibson was the dominant personality of the pair and the one whose testimony would prove more significant. At the bench, the defense attorneys had asked to postpone her testimony until the next morning so that it would not be interrupted, and the prosecuting attorney had agreed. She would be the first witness on the third day of the trial.

XI

THE NIGHT brought a sharp thunderstorm, and sheets of slippery, wet leaves covered the streets the next morning. Colder weather followed the storm, and it was a gray, wet morning, with gray and dark gray clouds flying low in the chill wind, as we entered the trial's third day. It was so dark that the courtroom needed lights. Nevertheless, more people were present than on either of the previous mornings. By nine o'clock all the seats were filled, and a few younger men and women were standing along the wall in the rear.

They had come to hear Ruth Gibson testify. When she was brought in from the jail the babble in the courtroom subsided as everyone turned to look at her. She, as always, ignored the spectators but seated herself beside Bob Day and began to talk with him as though they were alone. I knew he had spent an hour with her in the jail the evening before and had come in before eight o'clock this morning to confer again with her before she took the stand. There was a feeling, manifest not only among the spectators but in the principals also, that her testimony would be the climax of the trial. She knew it, could not help knowing it, and I was not alone in my fascination with her demeanor. She was as calm as anyone in the room. The instinct for self-preservation must have sustained her.

As soon as the court was in session Bob Day arose and announced that Ruth Gibson would testify in her own defense. She rose and walked across the front of the courtroom to the stand. She was dressed differently this morning, in a white short-sleeved blouse and blue skirt, small white shoes—the kind they call ballerina slippers, I think—and no stockings. She was wearing a little lipstick and no other makeup; no jewelry. She held a small handkerchief in her hand. I suspect she had planned for days before deciding what to wear on this occasion. In my opinion, she had chosen well.

The clerk came forward. Ruth raised her right hand and swore to tell the truth, the whole truth, and nothing but the truth, so help her God.

She took her place in the chair, crossed her legs at the ankles, and rested her hands in her lap.

"State your full name, please," said Bob Day as he walked across the room to stand at the rail of the jury box.

"Ruth Elaine Gibson," she replied in a clear, calm voice.

"Your place of residence?"

She hesitated a moment, drew a breath, and said, "The county jail."

Bob smiled and said, "No, I mean where do you live when you are not in jail?" I would have phrased the question better.

Ruth ran her tongue over her lips. "My family lives out in the country," she said. "I work in town and live with Mrs. Cummins on Bridge Street."

"How old are you, Ruth?"

"I'm twenty-two."

"How much education do you have, Ruth?"

"I had to quit high school when I was a junior, when I was seventeen."

"Why?"

"I had to go to work."

"How long have you lived and worked in Alexandria?"

"It's been about three years."

"I was a waitress at Reitlinger's restaurant."

"And where do you work and what do you do?"

Ruth was plainly a carefully rehearsed witness. She spoke with the same unnatural precision that Paul Russell had. I suppose witnesses can speak precisely, but it sounds artificial to me. Juries know it when people talk unnaturally.

"Now, first," said Bob, "to clear the air, let me ask you this. Did you have anything to do with the alleged robbery of De-Witt's Jewelry Store which is supposed to have occurred on May twentieth?"

Ruth Gibson drew herself very erect and in a studied tone said forcefully, "No, I did not."

"Did you assist Roger Louis or anyone else to commit a robbery of DeWitt's Jewelry Store?"

"No, sir."

"Did you ever plan or plot a robbery or theft from DeWitt's Jewelry Store?"

"No, sir."

"Did you ever suggest or propose to Paul Russell or anyone else that you and he steal from DeWitt's Jewelry Store?"

"No, I did not," she said emphatically. As she sat up and drew back her shoulders and forcefully answered Bob's questions, the jury saw in the drape of her blouse the only suggestion it ever saw of her ample breasts. She was also being modest. Her blouse was loose and of a material sufficiently opaque that the most strait-laced member of the jury could not accuse her of too much show. Her skirt was short and uncovered her knees when she sat, but she kept it under control. I am told that this did not concern her in other circumstances.

"Are you, however, acquainted with Paul Russell, or Doc Russell, as he is called?"

"Yes, I am."

"How long have you known him?"

"About a year, I guess."

"Where and in what circumstances did you become acquainted with him?"

"He used to come in the restaurant, and I waited on him many times."

"Did he talk to you when you waited on him?"

"Yes, he did."

"What did he say?"

"Well, he used to kid around and tell jokes. Then he started asking me to go out with him."

"What was your response to that?"

"Well, I said no to him several times, and then finally I said I'd go out with him."

"When was that?"

"I'm not sure when it was exactly," said Ruth slowly. "It was after the first of the year, in January, I suppose."

"Tell us about your first date."

"Well, it was on my night off. He came and picked me up at the house. He brought me a little bottle of perfume. He took me to a movie, and then after the movie he took me to the Alexandria Bar and Grill for a drink, and we had a couple of drinks together. He ordered champagne cocktails. It was the first time I'd ever had anything like that. Then we went out in his car, and he drove out in the country and parked."

At this point she paused, and Bob Day pressed her by asking, "And then what happened?"

"Well," she said, and her voice trailed off a little, "he wanted to neck. He . . . he wanted to do more than that too."

"Speak up, Ruth," said Bob Day. "What happened?"

"Well," she said, and she licked her lips and caught up her breath, "he kissed me and he felt me all over with his hands, and he tried to take my clothes off."

"And what did you do?"

"I let him kiss me," she said. She was speaking forcefully again, determined, it appeared, to say what she had to say. "It seemed like I should. He had brought me a present and bought me champagne. But I tried to stop him from doing any more."

"And what happened?"

"I couldn't stop him too well. When I'd get a hold of one of his hands and pull it off me he'd put the other one somewhere. He kind of laughed about it and went ahead."

"Did you tell him to stop?"

"Yes, but he just laughed at me."

"Did he put his hands on your breasts?"

"Yes," she said, nodding her head.

"And on your legs?"

"Yes."

"Ruth, do you know what part of your body I mean when I use the term genitals?" Bob asked seriously.

"Yes," she said and nodded.

"Did he put his hands on your genitals?"

"He tried to, but I would always fight him off."

"Was he putting his hands inside your clothes?"

"No, outside."

"Did he try to put his hands inside your clothes?"

"Yes, and he tried to take my clothes off. That's when I got mad and hit him and got out of the car."

"You hit him and got out of the car?" Bob Day repeated.

"Yes, I did," she said.

"Then what happened?"

She relaxed a little, and she said, "Well, then he got out of the car and came to me and said he was sorry. He promised he wouldn't do it again."

"Then what happened?"

"We got back in the car and went back to town. He took me home then."

"Did you go out with him again?"

"Yes, he came to the restaurant and offered to drive me home after work the next day. He said he'd be a gentleman, and he was. He was real nice after that."

"You continued seeing him?"

"Yes."

"Describe the relationship."

"Well," she said, pausing to search for words, "he was real nice to me for a while. He took me home from work, and he took me to nice places. And he brought me presents, like a little bracelet. He told me he liked me a lot, and I liked him a lot too. But he kept on wanting to do more. He was never satisfied, and he wanted me always to let him do more."

"You mean," Bob interrupted, "he wanted to have sexual intercourse with you?"

Ruth nodded. "He was leading up to that. He'd talk me into

letting him do one thing, and he'd say that was it, if I'd do that he wouldn't ask for any more, but then as soon as I'd let him, he'd want to do something else. He just kept on that way."

"Did he undress you?"

"Yes, and we had to run the car motor all the time and run the heater because it was so cold. It was cold even with the heater." When she added this last comment there was laughter in the courtroom.

"Did you have sexual intercourse with him?"

"Once," she said simply.

"Why did you break up with him?" Bob asked.

She sat up again and drew back her shoulders. "He wanted to do it all the time, nothing else but that all the time, every time I saw him. And he wanted me to do other things too, even more than that. And I wouldn't, and we argued and fought about it all the time."

"Did you break it up, or did he?"

"One night he told me he wouldn't go out with me anymore if I wouldn't do what he wanted me to do, so I said okay. That was the end of it."

"Did he ever tell you he loved you?"

"He'd say that when he was arguing me into doing something."

"Did you love him?"

"I guess I did for a while," she said quietly, after a slight hesitation that interrupted what had been a rapid exchange of questions and answers. "But it got so I couldn't stand all the arguing. He wanted me to do whatever he wanted or else."

"Did you ever talk to him about taking money from the store?"

"No," she said, "I never did that."

"Did he ever say anything to you about that?"

"No."

"All right," said Bob. He walked back to his place and sat down. "Let's talk about the day when a robbery was supposed to have taken place. To begin with, did you have to work that Saturday?"

"No, Saturday was my day off that week."

"What arrangements had you made for your day off?"

"Well, by then I was going with Roger Louis all the time, and he was out fishing for the weekend on Greenwater Creek. He was supposed to come into town to pick me up and take me out there with him."

"What time was he supposed to come for you?"

"Ten-thirty or eleven. I worked the night before and I wanted to sleep late."

"Did he come?"

"Yes."

"At what time?"

"I don't know exactly. When I expected him. Before eleven."

"Where was Mrs. Cummins when Roger came for you?"

"I don't know. She wasn't home when I got up. She used to go shopping on Saturday mornings."

"Where did Roger take you?"

"Well, he told me the fishing was no good and they had decided to quit, so we couldn't go out there. We sat in front of the house in the car and talked a while, and he asked me if I wanted to go up to the old house, and I said I would if he wanted to. So we went up there."

Ruth spoke very carefully, thoughtfully drawing her answers out of her memory, and showing no preference for one question over another.

"Why did you go there?"

"Because it was a place where we could go and be by ourselves."

"Did you go there for the purpose of having sexual intercourse?"

Ruth looked at the jury, as if trying to judge their reaction, and then she looked at her attorney and said, "Yes."

"And did you have sexual intercourse there that day?"

"Yes."

"What were you doing when you heard the sheriff's car come up the road?"

"We were having sexual intercourse."

The members of the jury were looking at her, steadily, quietly, with neither approval or disapproval on any of their faces. Searching for their reaction to her story, she stared at the jurors, but she could not find any. She had prepared herself to tell this part of the story, but even so she was telling it only with some effort. Her effort now became apparent in her voice and face, even in her posture. It had broken the calm.

"What happened then?"

"We didn't pay any attention at first, but then we heard the car stop. We listened for a minute or two, and then Roger got out of bed and looked out the window. He said he couldn't see anything. I got up and put on my shorts and blouse. We kept quiet and kept looking. Then we saw the sheriff and Mike Bradstreet climbing up the hill, sneaking up, sort of crouched down and coming quiet. I was scared to death. I just ran. Roger hollered at me to wait, but I just ran."

"Why did you run?" Bob Day interrupted.

"I thought," she said hesitantly, looking down at the floor, "I thought it was against the law for me to let him do what he had been doing, and I thought they would put me in jail for doing that. So I was scared, and I ran away."

"Then what happened?"

"They chased us. I couldn't run very fast because I didn't have any shoes, and besides, somebody shot off a gun and I thought they were shooting at us, so I stopped and laid down behind a log. Then they caught up with me, and the sheriff put his handcuffs on my legs, and they went on after Roger."

"Did you try to get away while they were off looking for Roger?"

"I tried to walk back down to the house, but I couldn't get down a steep place and I fell down."

"What happened then?"

"The sheriff came back after a while and took the handcuffs off me and took me down to the house, and then he handcuffed me to the bed while he went around searching the house."

"Did anyone tell you, either then or while you were in the car on the way back to town, what the charge against you was?"

"No, they didn't say."

"And what did you think it was?"

"I thought they had arrested me for letting Roger have sex relations with me."

"Did you think you would go to prison for that?"

"I had always heard you would," she said apologetically, as if to indicate she knew better now.

"When was the first time you realized you were charged with armed robbery?"

"When we got into the sheriff's office the sheriff said to Chloe something about here's the girl that robbed the jewelry store, or something like that. That's the first I knew that that's what I was charged with."

"Have you ever said to anyone, Tom Miller or anyone else, that you committed this crime?"

"No, sir, because that wouldn't be so. I didn't."

Bob Day turned to Baumgardner and said, "You may cross-examine."

"Well, now, young lady, we have lots of things to talk about," said Joe Baumgardner casually, shuffling his notes. "How long have you been in jail?"

"Ever since. Five months," said Ruth quietly.

"Five months ago, out there on Shambles Ridge in that house where you let Roger Louis do the things you wouldn't let Doc Russell do, were you in love with Roger?" asked Baumgardner, still casual, raising his eyebrows and holding his mouth slightly open after he had asked his question.

"Yes," said she.

"You were? Well, are you in love with him now?"

"Not any more," she said positively.

"Well, how is that? Has he been running around on you while you have been in jail?"

"I don't know. I just don't feel that way about him any more."

"I see. Well, for how long a period did you feel that way about him?"

"I don't know exactly."

"Well, was it just that one day?"

"No."

"Several days?"

"More than that."

"Well, now let's see," said Baumgardner, looking at his notes. "When did you last go out with Paul Russell?"

"In March, I think it was."

"End of March?"

"Yes, or the first of April."

"Were you going out with Roger at the same time?"

"No."

"Well, when did you first start going out with Roger?"

"Right after I quit going out with Paul Russell."

"All right. First of April, then?"

"Yes," she agreed.

"Was May twenty the first time you had let Roger have sexual intercourse with you?"

"No."

"For how long had you been letting him do that?"

"I don't know."

"Well, Ruth, is letting a man have intercourse with you a matter of some importance to you?"

"Yes."

"Then you should be able to tell us with some degree of accuracy when you first let Roger do it."

"Well, I don't know exactly," she insisted. "I can't say what day of what month it was."

"Well, how long had you been going out with him when it first happened?"

"I don't know. Three weeks or so, I guess."

"All right. Three weeks after you started going out with Roger Louis you let him have sexual relations with you. Is that right?"

"Yes," she said softly, and Baumgardner looked at her and apparently thought of making her admit it more loudly, but he reconsidered the idea and went on.

"Now, you say you had intercourse with Paul Russell once. How long had you been going out with him at that time?"

"About the same."

"About three weeks? That's about par for the course, then? Tell me, Ruth, when Paul Russell had intercourse with you, was that your first time?"

"Objection," said Bob Day.

"Well, now, your honor," said Baumgardner. "This girl's chastity has become an issue in the case. I didn't intend that it should become an issue, but the defense has made it so. She says she resisted Russell but surrendered to Louis. We will have to know if Russell ruined a virgin."

"I'm afraid," said Judge Kemp grimly, "that it has become an issue. I'll have to overrule the objection."

"The question," said Baumgardner, "was if your experience with Paul Russell was your first. Was it?"

"No," said Ruth Gibson plainly.

"Well, you were not a virgin then?"

"No."

"May I ask how many men had enjoyed your favors before Paul Russell?"

"Objection," exclaimed Bob Day. "Now he is going too far."

"I'm afraid not," said the judge. "You may answer."

"Two or three," said Ruth Gibson quickly.

"Two *or* three?" asked Baumgardner incredulously. "Don't you remember how many?"

"Three," said Ruth. She was uncomfortable but calm.

"All right," said the prosecutor. "We will accept that. Now, you said you liked Paul Russell; he was nice to you, right?"

"Yes."

"Then why did you deny him what you had given to three other men before?"

Ruth looked down for a moment, and her tongue came out and curled down over her lower lip for an instant. She wiped that lower lip with her handkerchief, and said, "Well, I didn't like him that well, for one thing. Besides that, he was so pushy about it. He tried to force me. And he wouldn't even be satisfied with that but wanted me to do a lot of other things, dirty things. I got disgusted with him."

"But you continued to go out with this disgusting young man?"

"Well," she said, "he could be so nice when he wanted to."

Joe Baumgardner lifted himself from his chair and walked over toward the witness. "Ruth," he said, "this jury is going to decide whether you spend the next several years of your life in prison. Do you want to tell them that you argued and fought and finally broke up with Paul Russell because he wanted you to submit to sexual relations with him, when you had let three other men do it before and when you let a fourth man do it within

233

three weeks after you started seeing him? Do you want to tell this jury that you have allowed five men to have intercourse with you but fought with one of them about it? Is that what you want this jury to believe?"

"I can't help it. It's true," she said aggressively, with some irritation. "Besides, I said it wasn't just *that* he wanted to do. I might have gone along with just that."

Baumgardner faced her and stood with his hands on his hips. "That's the way you're going to leave it?"

"It's true," she said quietly.

Baumgardner shrugged, turned his back on her, and returned to his seat. He had found out one thing: she would not scare.

"What did you mean when you said you might have gone along with just that?" asked Baumgardner.

"When I said what?" she asked.

"When you said, in response to my question a moment ago, that you might have gone along with Paul Russell if he had wanted just that. What is that?"

Ruth Gibson was confused. After a moment she said, "I don't know what I said. You made me mad for a minute."

"I can have the reporter read the question and answer," Baumgardner offered.

Bob Day rose. "If the court please," he said, "this has gone far enough. I object to the question."

"I must overrule the objection," said the judge. "But I do agree that it would be better to go on to something else."

"Well, I will ask you this," said the prosecutor. "Do you want to testify that if all Paul Russell had wanted to do with you was have sexual intercourse and no other sexual experiments you might have permitted it? Is that what you meant to say?"

"I don't remember saying anything like that," said Ruth.

"All right," said Baumgardner. "We'll drop it."

He had damaged Ruth Gibson a bit there. The jury had caught what she said, and it did not look good for her to plead that she did not know what Baumgardner was talking about. It looked as though she were trying to lie out of something.

It would be hard to say what effect all this testimony about sex had. Some jurors are undoubtedly prejudiced by revelations of the sex life of a defendant, but I could not hazard a guess about any of these jurors. Linda Tubman, for one, was a girl the same age and of the same background as Ruth Gibson. She may have been hearing of experiences similar to her own. Others on the jury were older people, women with families, and their attitudes might have been strongly affected. It is speculation. You can never know.

"Were you ever in DeWitt's store?" Baumgardner asked.

"Yes. Several times. Many times."

"Did you talk to Paul Russell when you were there?"

"Well, I had been in there before I started going out with him, and I didn't talk to him then. But during the time when I was going out with him I talked to him when I was in the store."

"Did you ever buy anything there?"

"I bought a wrist watch once," she said.

"When was that?"

"A year or so ago."

"Did you buy anything the times you went in when you were going with Paul?"

"No."

"Why did you go in there then?"

"To see him."

"To talk about stealing from the store?"

"No."

"To look around and plan a way of stealing from the store?"

"No," said she strongly.

"Now, do I understand you to say that on Saturday, May twenty, it was your original plan to go out on Greenwater Creek where Roger and two of his friends were fishing?"

"That's right."

"Did you plan to take along a fishing pole of your own?"

"I don't have one."

"Do you like to fish?"

"Sure."

"But you don't have a pole?"

"No."

"How about a fishing license? Do you have that?"

"No."

"No pole and no license, but you like to fish?"

"That's right."

"Then you planned to spend the day fishing?"

"Well, yes."

"You seem to have some hesitation about it. What else did you plan to do?"

"I didn't plan anything."

"They were going to stay until Sunday, were they not?"

"Yes."

"Were you going to stay overnight too?"

"No."

"And sleep in Roger's sleeping bag with him?"

"No."

"You were just going out fishing with three men?"

This series of questions and answers was very rapid, and Bob Day tried hard to catch Ruth's attention and slow her down. He had undoubtedly instructed her not to be led into exchanging answers and questions too quickly. He would want her to think about every answer before she spoke, no matter how readily the answer came to mind. A lawyer knows how hazardous a rapid exchange can be. The cross-examiner does not need time to think; he has made up the questions before. The witness needs time and should take it.

Baumgardner reached down into the cardboard carton which had sat beneath his table all during the trial and brought up what appeared to be a faded blue rag. He took it up to Ruth and handed it to her and asked, "Can you identify those?"

"Those are my shorts," she said, and then she added ruefully, "which somebody stole out of my cell a week ago."

"Would you gentlemen care to identify State's Exhibit B?" Baumgardner asked the two defense attorneys. They shook their heads, and he said, "Your Honor, we ask that this pair of shorts be admitted into evidence as State's Exhibit B."

"It will be admitted."

Baumgardner handed the shorts to the reporter, who attached a yellow paper tag to them and handed them back to him. He gave them back to Ruth Gibson.

"Were you wearing those shorts when you went out with Roger that Saturday morning?"

"Yes."

"Would you mind standing up and holding them up before you, so the jury can see them?"

Ruth Gibson rose and held the shorts before her hips. It was plain that they were brief.

"You were going to wear these out fishing?"

"Yes."

"All right. Thank you. You may sit down. When the sheriff searched the house on Shambles Ridge he found some other clothing of yours, which I have there in my box. What were you doing with that?"

"I took some other things with me so we could go out that evening if we wanted to and I wouldn't have to go back to change."

"I see. And your underclothing?"

"I didn't have time to put that on before I ran out the door."

"All right. Now, you say you decided to go up to the house on the ridge when you found out you could not go fishing?"

"Yes."

"And you went there for the express purpose of having sexual intercourse?" said the prosecutor loudly, punctuating with a jerky nod.

"Yes."

"And you did so?" he said the same way.

"Yes," she answered quietly, calmly.

"Roger testified that between eleven o'clock when you arrived there and one o'clock when the sheriff arrived you had sexual intercourse two or three times. Is that right?"

"Yes."

"Which was it, two or three times?"

"Twice."

"And the sheriff interrupted you the second time?"

"Yes."

"And this was not the first time you had gone to that house and done the same thing?"

"No."

"All right," said Baumgardner, reducing his voice. "Now when you heard the sheriff's car you got out of bed and looked out; right?"

237

"Yes."

"Then you saw the sheriff and his deputy coming toward the house?"

"Yes."

"Then you ran?"

"Yes."

"Why?" he asked shortly.

Ruth drew in her breath and began patiently to explain. "I thought," she said slowly and emphatically, gesturing with her hands, "that it was against the law to have sex relations when you aren't married. I thought they had come to arrest us for that, and I was scared and I ran. That's all."

"How do you suppose the sheriff knew you were there in the first place—and indulging in sexual intercourse in the second place?" Baumgardner asked his question in a loud and insistent voice.

"I didn't have much time to think about it, but I supposed they saw the car and knew nobody lived in the house. They probably figured that somebody was up there doing what we were doing."

It was an infinitely better answer than Roger Louis had had for the question. Baumgardner went back to his seat and sat down.

"Did you really think you could get away, running out of the house without your shoes and leaving a car with license plates behind you?" he asked in a tired, exhaled voice.

"I was too scared to think. If I had thought about it, I wouldn't have run."

"You would call what you felt panic?"

"Yes."

"Did you ever hear of anyone being arrested for having pre-marital intercourse?"

"I always heard they did."

"But did you ever hear of any specific person getting in trouble for that?"

"I've heard of fellows going to the penitentiary for having relations with girls."

"With girls twenty-two years old?"

"I don't know how old the girls were."

Schwallie, juror number eleven, could not, apparently, repress a snicker. It was plain that Baumgardner was up against an antagonist far superior in intelligence to Roger Louis. Of course, she had heard the cross-examination of Louis and had had a night to think about her answers.

"All right," said Baumgardner. "You want this jury to believe that you ran out the door of that house in a panic because you thought the sheriff had come to arrest you for having sexual relations with Roger Louis?"

"It's true," she said, shaking her head.

"You heard Roger admit that it's ridiculous."

"I can't help that. It wasn't ridiculous to me then," Ruth said calmly.

"And what did you suppose the penalty was for having sexual intercourse with a man to whom you were not married?"

"I didn't know."

"A long term in prison?"

"I don't know."

"Come on now, Ruth," said Joe Baumgardner. "The jury can see you're too intelligent to believe something like that." Ruth did not reply. She looked to Bob Day and lifted her shoulders slightly, questioningly.

Baumgardner rose and walked over to confront her again. "Have you ever sold your sexual favors for money?" he asked suddenly.

"No," she answered angrily.

"Have you ever used your sex or the offer of it to get men to do things for you?"

"No!" she said again heatedly.

"Well, let me ask you what you meant when you asked Mike Bradstreet to let you go and told him you would give him all kinds of cooperation if he did. What did you mean by that?"

. "I don't remember saying that."

"You heard Mike testify that you did. Do you deny you said it?"

"No," she said tentatively. "But I don't remember saying it."

239

"Well, will you accept Mike Bradstreet's testimony that you said it?"

She looked down for a moment and then up again and said, "I guess so." I could see Bob Day wince.

"Well then, what did you mean by that?"

"Since I don't remember saying it, I can't remember what I might have meant," said Ruth.

"That's very clever of you." Baumgardner sneered. "You have a convenient memory, don't you?"

She did not answer.

"Well, do you remember telling the sheriff you were not Ruth Gibson?" asked Baumgardner with exaggerated emphasis, facing her dramatically.

"Yes," she said.

"Well, how do you explain away that?"

Ruth opened her hands in a gesture of innocence. "I don't know for sure. I thought he'd let me go and my family wouldn't find out about it. I was scared. I didn't know what to say."

Her answers were too good. It was plain that she had anticipated nearly every question and had given some thought to her answers. I think the jury would have preferred to see her confused sometimes. On the other hand, during five months in jail she had had little else to think about, and who can condemn her for having prepared herself the best she could?

"Do you know Horace Miller, better known as Tom Miller?" Baumgardner asked.

"Yes."

"Have you had dates with him?" Baumgardner asked, walking away from her and returning to his seat.

"Yes."

"Did you have sexual intercourse with him?"

"No."

"Do you remember seeing him in the county jail during the month of June?"

"Yes."

"Did you talk to him?"

"Yes."

"Across the space between the men's and the women's jails?"

240

"Yes."

"Did you discuss the robbery?"

"Yes."

"Do you recall his using the words, 'Level with me now, honey,' or words to that effect?"

"Yes."

"He asked you whether you had actually committed the crime?"

"Yes."

"And what did you tell him?"

"I told him I didn't do it," said she without expression.

"And if he told me you said something else, he lied to me then?" pressed Baumgardner, gesturing.

"If he told you I said I did it, he lied to you," said Ruth.

"How long did you say you have been in jail?"

"Five months. Since May twentieth."

"Is it the first time you were ever in jail?"

"Yes."

"Do I understand you to say you were in love with Roger Louis five months ago?"

"Yes."

"What do you mean by being in love?"

She had not anticipated this question, and she thought for several moments before shrugging and saying, "I don't know how to say it exactly."

"Well, let me help you," said the prosecutor. "Did you intend to marry Roger Louis?"

"Well, we hadn't talked about that," she said.

"Had you thought about it?"

"No."

"Well, would you want to marry a man like that?"

"I thought I would then."

"Let's examine that a little," said Baumgardner. "You knew he drank too much, didn't you?"

"I didn't notice it."

"Did you know he had been convicted and sent to jail for drunken driving?"

"No."

"Did you know, for example, he had consumed the better part of a case of beer the night before he came to pick you up, or so he says?"

"No."

"Did you know about the bad check he wrote for Peter Showalter?"

"No."

"Did you know he was repeatedly having his wages attached by people to whom he owed money?"

"I knew that."

"Did you know about the night when he tried to pull the panties off his friend's wife?"

"No, I never heard of that before."

"Well, you didn't know much about the man you say you loved, did you?"

"Apparently not," she admitted, with a wan little smile.

"You have testified that you disliked Paul Russell because he was too aggressive. Roger Louis was having intercourse with you within three weeks after your first date. Wasn't that aggressive?"

"Not the same way, no."

"What was the difference?"

"Objection," said Bob Day. "All this is irrelevant."

"Not if it shows that she was not in love with Louis at all but only recruited him for the robbery she had planned," said Baumgardner.

"The objection must be overruled," said Judge Kemp.

"What was the difference?" repeated Baumgardner.

"I don't know if I can tell you," said Ruth Gibson, betraying some confusion and with a suggestion of protest in her voice.

"Well, was he more tender with you? Did he bring you nicer gifts? Was he more thoughtful?" asked Baumgardner, looking all the while at the scowling, hunched little figure of Louis and by his contemptuous look inviting the jury to compare Louis with Russell.

"I don't know," Ruth said quickly, her voice rising slightly.

"Were you in love with him when you first let him have intercourse with you?"

"Yes."

"You wouldn't have let him have intercourse with you if you hadn't been in love with him, is that right?" Baumgardner pressed quickly, trying to extract a quick answer.

"No, I wouldn't," she said immediately.

"Well then, were you in love with Paul Russell when you let him?"

"Yes, for a little while I was."

"And with each of the other three men you testified have had relations with you?"

"Yes, I guess so."

"You guess so? Don't you know?"

"It's hard to know what you feel," Ruth said.

"Well, how old were you when you lost your virginity?" the prosecutor asked, drawing the back of his hand across his forehead.

"Seventeen."

"And you were in love with the fellow?"

"I thought I was."

"Five times since you were seventeen, twice within two months this year, you have been sufficiently in love with a man to let him have sexual intercourse with you. Is that right?"

"I guess so," she said on indrawn breath.

"Were you and any of these fellows planning marriage?"

"We never talked about it."

"You never talked about marriage, and yet you say you were in love. What does love mean to you, Ruth? Just intercourse? Is that your definition of it?" Baumgardner asked. He raised his shoulders and put his palms together and spoke in a drawn, protesting voice.

"Objection," said Bob Day. "This has gone 'way beyond any possible relevance."

"I will allow one or two more questions to establish relevance," said the judge.

"How long does love last, Ruth?" asked Baumgardner, pressing while he could. "You were in love with Russell in March and with Louis in April and with no one in October. You put it on and take it off pretty easy, don't you?"

"Objection!" insisted Bob Day with some irritation.

The judge ruled without waiting to hear the reason for the objection. "Strike that question from the record," he said. "Make it relevant, Mr. Baumgardner, and finish it up."

"Well, Ruth, I will just ask you this," said Joe Baumgardner quietly and with a tone of finality. "Do you want this jury to believe that you were in love with . . . that?" He swung his arm around toward Louis.

Ruth looked in the direction the prosecutor pointed, at the dark figure of Louis, who stared back at her from beneath his brows and seemed to defy her to deny him. For a long, tense minute she just looked and did not speak.

"Well?" said Baumgardner sharply.

Ruth Gibson turned to the prosecutor, drew in her breath, sat up and threw back her shoulders, and in a clear voice she said, "Yes, I was."

"All right," said Baumgardner. "If that's the way you want it. Let's talk about money." He selected from his file a sheet of notes and laid it out before him. "How much did you make working at Billy's?"

"Thirty dollars a week and tips," said the girl.

"How much would tips come to each week, on the average?"

"Fifteen, twenty dollars. Sometimes more."

"How much did your room cost you?"

"Twelve dollars a week."

This line of questioning was dry compared to what had preceded it, and both prosecutor and witness seemed to take it for a moment to relax.

"Were you satisfied with what you were making?"

"Well, I always wanted to do better."

"Isn't it a fact that you did a lot of complaining, to lots of different people, about your station in life?"

Ruth ran first her tongue and then her teeth over her lower lip. "Well," she said, "I wasn't getting anywhere very fast."

"You wanted to buy a car, didn't you?"

"Yes."

"How much were you able to save toward it?"

"Nothing."

"But you shopped around, priced some used cars?"

"Yes."

"Tell us about a black Mercury you looked at on a lot down on Franklin Street," he said, laying out a sheet of paper covered with notes to which was clipped a carbon copy of a subpoena.

"I looked at a car there, a black Mercury," she said.

"Did you have the money to buy it?"

"No."

"Did you take it out and drive it around?"

"Yes, the man let me."

"What did you tell him about the money to buy it?"

"I don't know what you mean."

"Well, did you tell him you would get the money to buy that car if you had to steal it? Did you say that?"

"Well, I didn't mean it," Ruth said with a little smile. She had admitted it. Baumgardner would not need to call the salesman to testify. He put the subpoena aside.

"When was it you told the man that?"

"I don't know exactly."

"In May?"

"I expect it was."

"You didn't like being a waitress, did you?"

She did not reply. She looked at Bob Day and then back to Baumgardner. The judge looked down at her, and MacInroth, who had been studying his notes, raised his head in the sudden silence to see what had stopped the exchange of questions and answers.

"Well?" said Baumgardner finally.

"Well," she said, almost whispering, and then she stopped and looked down.

"You will have to answer," said Judge Kemp.

"No, I didn't," said the girl in a voice barely audible.

"Why not?" asked Baumgardner quickly.

"It doesn't . . . exactly lead to anywhere," she answered in a small voice.

"Well, where was it you had in mind you wanted to go, Ruth?"

She raised her head and spoke out again. "I don't know. I just wanted to be somebody."

"No," Baumgardner contradicted her. "I think you had some specific ideas about where you wanted to go. Do you want to tell us about that?"

"I don't know what you're talking about," she said.

"All right," said Joe Baumgardner, drawing in his breath and feigning some impatience. "Suppose I tell you. What were you and Sally Druro planning to do?"

"That was just talk!" Ruth Gibson burst out, shaking her head.

MacInroth looked up from his notes again. Bob Day put his hand before his mouth and tried to catch his client's attention. Ruth, however, fixed her eyes on Baumgardner, and for the first time she was plainly and openly unhappy with the course of the cross-examination. She had raised her voice for the first time, and now she thrust her head forward on her shoulders, and the muscles in her neck stood out like hard cords.

"Well, what was that just talk about?" Baumgardner asked immediately.

"It was only talk, that's all," she said again in a rising voice.

"Well, what was it about?" repeated Baumgardner.

"We just talked about going away," said Ruth nervously, shaking her hands loosely in a deprecating gesture.

"Going away where?"

Ruth took a breath and said, "To California," in an exhaled voice.

"What were you going to do in California?"

"We were going to get some other kind of a job."

"What kind of a job?"

"Any kind of a job."

Joe Baumgardner nodded. "Anything but being a little waitress in a little restaurant in a little town, huh?"

She nodded.

"You had some thought of being a model, maybe even an actress, is that it?"

"No," said Ruth quietly. "I didn't think that. Not me."

"Anyway, you say it was just talk, and you and Sally never really meant to go, hey?"

"It was just talk," said Ruth sadly.

"Well, Sally had saved enough money to go, hadn't she?"

· "I guess so," said Ruth, her voice still nervous.

"Well, she showed you the money she had saved to go, didn't she?"

"Yes."

"She wasn't just talking then, was she?"

"I guess not."

"When did Sally plan to leave?"

"The first of June."

"All right. Now, Ruth, Sally doesn't want to come in here and testify against you, so do you want to tell us yourself what you said to Sally when she showed you her money and asked you if you were going to go with her?"

"It was only just talk," Ruth insisted in a high, protesting voice, shaking her head.

"Well, what did you say to her?" asked Joe Baumgardner, pointing at her with a shaking finger.

"I told her—" Ruth said, and then she stopped and lowered her head. "I said"—she began again, speaking into her lap—"I told her I'd have the money and go with her."

The prosecuting attorney backed slowly away from the witness stand and took a place standing at the rail of the jury box. He waited until she raised her head. "And how much money did you have to go to California on, Ruth?"

"None," she whispered. She drew deep breaths to recover control of her voice.

"What else did you tell Sally about going to California? About how you were going to go?"

"I told her," said the witness in a wavering voice, "I would buy that car and drive out."

"Did you tell her that by June first you would have enough money to buy the car and go to California?"

Ruth nodded, wiping at her eyes.

"Well, where did you plan to get the money?"

"I don't know," she said, shaking her head. Then she raised her voice and added, "I didn't really think I could go."

"Did you tell Roger about your plans to go to California?"

"No."

"Was it your plan to stay in California long?"

247

"I don't know," she managed to say, fighting down sobs.

"You didn't really plan to come back at all, did you?"

"That was the way we talked about it." It was a whisper, but the jury heard it.

"But you didn't tell the man you loved anything about it?"

"No."

"All right. That's all," said Joe Baumgardner abruptly.

Ruth Gibson sat still as though she did not comprehend what the prosecuting attorney had said. She watched him return to his seat, and she kept looking toward him as though she expected more questions. At last she looked to Bob Day, and he raised a finger and gestured that she should come back to her place beside him. She turned toward the jury and cast her eyes over them, her lips parted slightly as though she were about to speak, then finally she stepped down and walked back to the defense table. She said nothing to her lawyer.

"Defense rests," said MacInroth.

"Will you want to offer anything in rebuttal?" Judge Kemp asked Baumgardner, and Baumgardner shook his head. "The court will stand in recess for one half hour," said the judge.

With that pronouncement, the courtroom burst into action as people hurried out to relieve themselves and to satisfy their hunger for tobacco. In the midst of the commotion mine were not the only eyes which remained fixed on Ruth Gibson, who now sat slack in her chair and looked tired as she had not looked before. I know what she felt because I have felt it. It is miserable to have to anticipate and plan for months for some brief performance of yours by which others will judge you, and then to perform, and then to have to sit and await their judgment. You review what you did or said, and inevitably you are disappointed in yourself. You suffer, in short; and if you had approached your hour, as Ruth Gibson undoubtedly did, with unrealistic notions of all the good you could do your cause, then you suffer proportionately more. Add to that the stake she had in what was happening, and you begin to understand what she felt. I should imagine in almost all her waking moments during the past five months her thoughts had touched on her hour before the jury. Now she had spoken to them. It was over.

No one, I think, could deny she was a surprisingly good witness. If she had a fault, it was probably, as I have commented before, that she was almost too good. She was so good that some people called it brazen. Some people asserted that no one could be so calm and tell the truth in her situation. They called her confidence the necessary confidence of a liar. No doubt such opinion was represented on the jury.

We had now almost reached that point in the trial when all attention would shift to the jury. Only two more procedural steps remained before the case actually went to the jury: the final arguments of counsel, and the judge's charge.

XII

Wʜᴇɴ ᴡᴇ ʀᴇᴛᴜʀɴᴇᴅ to court, Joe Baumgardner rose to open the final argument for the state. He was dressed in a brown suit, and he did not button the coat across his belly, so that his shirt stretched tightly across the broad, convex curve of his stomach. When he rose he was lifting a weight, so he got to his feet slowly and with a certain dignity; and yet he was a jolly man, as fat Germans are supposed to be. People liked him, and I am sure the jury had learned to like him during the two and a half days of the trial. Holding in his hand a yellow legal pad, he stood and faced them as he began to speak.

"Ladies and gentlemen of the jury," he said formally and slowly, but still with a small smile on his face and in his voice, "we have now reached that point in the trial where it becomes the duty of the attorneys representing the prosecution and the defense to speak to you and to argue the case. I will talk to you first, and then the two gentlemen representing the defendants will speak to you, and then I will speak to you briefly again. We do this because you have sat through more than two days of trial and have listened to thousands of words of testimony, and now the two sides will try to explain to you what you have heard, to tell you what has been proved, and to tell you what verdict the evidence deserves. We represent, of course, two opposing sides, and while my duty is to the state and the people of this county, the duty of the two other attorneys is to their accused clients. Naturally we will not take the same view of what you have seen and heard. It is my position that the evidence entirely deserves a verdict of guilty and that it will be your duty to return such a verdict, but I have no doubt that my two opponents will take an opposite view of the case and will argue to you that the evidence calls for the acquittal of their clients. We will therefore argue before you, make an appeal to you for the verdict we think the evidence requires, and if our argument serves to lay emphasis on the more important points of all you have heard, if it serves to remove some of the confusion which may exist in your minds, if it serves to make the case as a whole more clear to you, then it will have served an important function in this trial and will have been well worth the time we spend on it. Such is the purpose of final argument."

Baumgardner moved back a step and rested his weight against the edge of his table. "In this first part of my argument," he said, "I want to review with you the evidence which has been placed before you. You will remember my opening statement, which I made to you more than two days ago. In that opening statement I told you the state would prove to you beyond any reasonable doubt that these two defendants were guilty of committing the armed robbery of DeWitt's store. I read the indictments to you, and I told you that the evidence would prove that Roger Louis and Ruth Gibson are guilty of the crimes charged in the indictments. Now let's look at the evidence and see what it proves. . . ."

Baumgardner began his review of the evidence by discussing the testimony of Paul Russell. Naturally he characterized it as truthful, and he professed some indignation at the attempt by the defendants to clear themselves by attacking Russell's character.

"If I were defending Roger Louis and Ruth Gibson," he said, "the testimony of Paul Russell would be a matter of deep concern to me, and I suppose I would have to do all I could to belittle Russell and his words. The motives of the defendants are therefore obvious. Nothing could suit their purpose so well as to have you believe that Paul Russell himself stole the missing money and jewelry. The trouble is, ladies and gentlemen"—and here the prosecutor bore down on his words—"the trouble is that not one shred of evidence so much as suggests any guilt on the part of Paul Russell. You are asked to believe he is guilty of a crime, not on the basis of any evidence, but only on the basis of a convenient innuendo which suits the purpose of the defense."

Baumgardner went on to make a telling point—that if Russell were accusing the two defendants only to cover himself, then he did it in a very hazardous way, because he had no way of knowing where Roger Louis and Ruth Gibson were that morning, and they might have had an unshakable alibi. As Baumgardner put it, "Ruth Gibson might have been in a supermarket where dozens of people would have seen her, and Roger Louis might have been in jail, for all Russell knew."

He went on to review the testimony of the other prosecution witnesses. Of course he stressed the fact that the two defendants had run away from the law.

"Several hours after the robbery the sheriff and Mike Bradstreet, acting on a hunch, arrived at the house on Shambles Ridge. Sure enough, Roger and Ruth were there. And what did Roger and Ruth do? When they saw the two law officers coming, they ran for the woods as fast as their legs would carry them. Why? Because, ladies and gentlemen," Joe Baumgardner thundered, enunciating each word alone before enunciating the next, "they knew why the sheriff had come. They were on the lam, and they had been found, and they ran: because they had robbed DeWitt's store, and their victim had seen Ruth Gibson, and they knew he had seen her, and they were running and hiding from the law, and here came the law. A signed confession would not have been better evidence of their guilt."

Joe Baumgardner paused to let his point sink in, and then he smiled. "That was a big mistake, to run like that," he said with a nod of his head and a little chuckle. "And they knew it after it was too late, after they had done it. So they invented a story to explain why they had done it. Not a very good story, not a very smart story, but a story. And having told that story they were stuck with it. They tell us, ladies and gentlemen, that they were interrupted in the act of intercourse, and because they were afraid that they would be sent to prison for having extramarital intercourse, they ran." Joe Baumgardner shook his head and smiled. "A couple of grown-up people. Not very smart, ladies and gentlemen, but smarter than that. It is a lie, ladies and gentlemen," he said, raising his voice grimly again. "In the first place, they saw the law officers when they were still down the hill quite a ways off. They had plenty of time to dress and break out a deck of cards and be sitting there playing gin when the sheriff and his deputy came in, and how would the law have known what they had been doing? In the second place, even if they were stupid enough to think—which you should not for a moment believe—that the sheriff had come for them because they were committing an immoral act, they could not possibly have thought they would be sent away for a long term for that. They did not panic out of fear of being caught in an immoral act. They panicked out of fear of being arrested for armed robbery and being convicted and being imprisoned for a long term."

"They knew they had been seen, that Paul Russell had identified Ruth," Baumgardner went on, lecturing the jury, counting off his points on his fingers, "that the law was after them. They went up to the house on Shambles Ridge because they could not go home, because they needed a place to hide at least until night, because they never dreamed the sheriff and his deputy would follow a lucky hunch and check the house on Shambles Ridge that very afternoon. Then they looked out the window, and lo and behold, who should be coming up the hill but the sheriff and a deputy! They were scared. They were deathly scared; they had reason to be. In a panic they ran, and when they did they admitted their guilt as much as if they had written a confession on a piece of paper and signed their names to it. The ridiculous story they made up to explain themselves only serves to further prove the point."

The argument followed the course which prosecutors' arguments usually take. He reviewed and summarized the state's case before proceeding to comment on the evidence offered by the defense.

Speaking of the case for the defense, Baumgardner indicated he would reserve most of his observations about the testimony of the defendants for the second part of his argument. Of the character witnesses he said:

"The trouble with character witnesses, ladies and gentlemen, is that they are chosen by the defense, and naturally they put on the stand only people they know will say the defendants are of good character. Who can know how many people they had to interview before they could get someone to say that Roger Louis and Ruth Gibson have good reputations? But even with that advantage of selection, the defense could not come up with convincing character witnesses. Roger's did not know much about him, did not know about his bad check, for example. Ruth's did not know about her sexual delinquency. What might even these selected witnesses have said if they had known the facts about their young friends?"

Then he commented on the testimony of MacKay and Drayer, the two alibi witnesses. He referred, of course, to the technique of cross-examination he had used, compelling them to go into the fine details of their story, and he spoke with blunt words of their inconsistencies. He reminded the jury of Drayer's criminal record. He talked about MacKay's selective memory.

"In short, ladies and gentlemen, the two of them are liars. They lied so obviously it didn't even require my cross-examination to show it. They are fumbling liars, not even clever, not even original in their lies. And yet, they are the best liars Roger Louis could recruit, so perhaps after all we should feel sorry for him for that. Almost. He concocted his lies in desperation, and these are the best liars he could find to tell them for him."

He summarized the case for the defense as resting only on the denials of the defendants, who of course would deny their guilt no matter how plain it was, and on the alibi sustained by no better testimony than that of MacKay and Drayer.

With that Baumgardner concluded the first part of his final argument. He would speak again after counsel for the defense had argued.

Joe Baumgardner was a capable man in argument. Possessed of that patience and good humor which is supposed to be characteristic of fat men, he hardly ever spoke in anger. He wandered about the front of the courtroom, yellow pad in hand, talking and tearing off used-up notes. He was never dull. His moods varied. His favorite mood was geniality; he argued with a smile, but he could also be grim. His chief talent, perhaps, was clarity. Many attorneys speak in long, involved sentences; their minds race ahead of their words and the intent and purpose of a sentence changes in mid-sentence, so they create monstrous examples of scrambled syntax and leave both meaning and understanding hanging in the air. But not Joe Baumgardner. He was effective. There was no denying it. The jury had listened carefully, and that is the surest sign.

The prosecutor sat down, and Bob Day rose. Carrying with him his yellow pad of notes, he walked to the witness stand and took his place there, resting the notes on the corner of the stand.

"Ladies and gentlemen," he said in a smooth, slight voice. "I do not stand here for the purpose of making an appeal for these two young people. I am not going to make a speech. The prosecuting attorney says the state rests its case on the evidence, and the defense will too. We are not afraid of the evidence. We see no need to obscure the facts."

People in the rear of the courtroom could not hear what he was saying, and there was some disturbance. He glanced back toward them, but he did not raise his voice. He was not talking to the crowd. Only to the jury. His manner and his voice were conversational. He made no gestures. His expression remained serious.

"This case boils down to one thing and one thing only," he went on. "In spite of anything we can say about it, in spite of every extraneous and emotional issue which has been injected into it, it still boils down to one thing. That one thing is this, ladies and gentlemen: Either you believe Paul Russell or you don't believe him."

Bob Day nodded his head, and he repeated, "Either you believe Paul Russell or you don't believe him. Because the testimony of Paul Russell is the only piece of evidence which has been introduced in this courtroom which supports the state's charge that Roger Louis and Ruth Gibson robbed DeWitt's store. If it were not for his testimony, we would not be here. If it were not for what Paul Russell says, Roger Louis would not be on trial in this courtroom today. If it were not for what he says, Ruth Gibson would not have spent five months in jail and would not be on trial in this courtroom today. I am sure it must be plain to you that the other evidence which the state has presented is all circumstantial and flimsy, and the prosecuting attorney would not have brought these people to trial on this charge if it had not been for the words of Paul Russell.

"That is the case for the state, ladies and gentlemen; that is all the case there is against Roger Louis and Ruth Gibson. The testimony of Paul Russell.

"Let me ask you: Do you think the state would have brought Roger Louis and Ruth Gibson into this courtroom and placed them on trial charged with armed robbery simply because they ran from the sheriff when he tried to arrest them? Or because Roger Louis and Ruth Gibson admittedly needed money? Or because Ruth Gibson had allowed men to have intercourse with her, about which the prosecutor has spoken so much? Or because Roger Louis at a drunken party acted less than gentlemanly with his friend's wife? Or because Roger Louis once wrote a bad check? Do you think that on any of those facts or a combination of all of them the state would have charged these two people with armed robbery?

"Or would you, as a jury, even for a moment imagine that those facts make a case for convicting these people and sending them to prison for armed robbery?

"No, ladies and gentlemen, these other elements of the state's case amount to nothing. Standing alone, they would not even justify our spending the time to try them. Without the testimony of one witness—Paul Russell—there is no case at all.

"Or let us suppose for a moment how the case would stand when you consider its inherent weaknesses without Paul Russell. For example, ladies and gentlemen, no attempt has even been made to explain what happened to the money and jewelry which are missing from DeWitt's store. If Roger Louis and Ruth Gibson took them, what did they do with them, and where are those things now? Where is the gun? Where is the blue jacket the supposed robber wore? Paul Russell suggests they may have disposed of them. Very well, if they had them maybe they did, but did the sheriff look for them? There has been no explanation whatever offered as to what became of the stolen property. Wouldn't you think someone would be interested to know?

"Why is it, ladies and gentlemen, that no witness but Paul Russell can be found to say there was a green 1950 Chevrolet on the street that morning? The chief of police told you how he inquired of people all along the street but found no one who had seen the car or the robber in the blue jacket. If this robbery happened, isn't it odd that no one can be found except Paul Russell who saw any part of it? With all the stores that were open on that street that morning, with all the people who must have been on the street, why is it that no one but Paul Russell saw the car or the robber?

"Ladies and gentlemen, even without mentioning the alibi supported by two disinterested witnesses, even taking the state's case alone without considering the defense, it is plain that it all rests on the testimony of the one witness, Paul Russell.

"Therefore, ladies and gentlemen," Bob Day went on, never moving from his place beside the witness stand, speaking always in the same quiet, reasoned way, "it is necessary for us to talk about Paul Russell. I will start by saying plainly that Paul Russell is a liar. It gives me no pleasure to say that, and I am sure it gives you none to hear it. I don't like to call a person a liar. I would rather think that he is mistaken and let it go at that, be polite about it. But you are being asked to send two young people to prison for long terms on the word of this Paul Russell, and in those circumstances we cannot afford to be polite. We cannot let our courteous aversion to the word liar prevent our using it where it fits."

Sometime during Joe Baumgardner's argument—I had not noticed just when—Paul Russell had come in and taken a seat about halfway to the front and to one side of the courtroom. Not everyone knew he was there, and I don't think any of the jury knew it, but the spectators who had noticed him were now looking to him for his reaction to Day's words. Russell's face was flushed and his jaw was set, and he looked at Bob Day and strained to hear what he was saying. Day did not know he was there.

"In the first place, ladies and gentlemen, let us speak of motive," said Bob Day. "Paul Russell has motive for lying. He is a clerk in a jewelry store. More than three thousand dollars' worth of jewelry and a considerable amount of cash are missing. It became a missing quantity at a time when Paul Russell was alone in the store. He says he was robbed, yet no one but him saw the robber, no one on a busy street saw the robber. No part of the missing jewelry and money has been recovered. In those circumstances, ladies and gentlemen, Paul Russell becomes a suspected thief. Fair or not, just or not, he cannot avoid suspicion. And he will be suspected until someone is found and convicted of the crime. If Roger Louis and Ruth Gibson are found not guilty, then the spotlight turns back on Paul Russell, and, ladies and gentlemen, he knows it. It is in his interest, his vital interest, to see these two people convicted. So even if he did not take the money himself, even if any accusation against him is unfair, Paul Russell has a strong motive to lie to you. When the prison gates close behind these two people, Paul Russell can relax. Not until."

There had developed an increasing intensity in Bob Day's argument. It is hard to describe. He spoke no louder, and his tones remained the same, but yet we could sense greater force behind his words, pressing them out and projecting them on the sensibilities of the jurors.

"There is reason, ladies and gentlemen, to think," he went on, "that the thief is Paul Russell himself, and that his motive in testifying falsely about Roger Louis and Ruth Gibson is simply to cover his own crime. It is obvious in the circumstances that he could be the guilty party. And there has been in his conduct more than one suggestion that he stole from his employer and made up a story to cover his own crime."

At this point Bob Day stopped for the first time. He took a deep breath. The jury was watching him. He had their attention.

"On this witness stand, testifying under oath, Paul Russell clearly demonstrated his dishonesty, ladies and gentlemen. He made himself out dishonest, and not in any minor respect. I ask you to recall his testimony about a proposition he said Ruth Gibson made to him that he rob the store for her. He told you under oath that she made that proposition to him many times, that finally he took it seriously, that he believed she meant it, that he believed she was capable of doing it. That is what he said. Then he was asked when he told Mr. Garfield, his employer, about this proposition to rob Mr. Garfield's store. And what did he say? He said, ladies and gentlemen, he never told Mr. Garfield. Mr. Garfield bore out that fact when he testified—Paul Russell never told him.

"Is that, ladies and gentlemen, the conduct of an honest employee? Someone makes a proposition to rob his employer's store, he believes the person means to do it and is capable of doing it, but he does not warn his employer. He does not give warning. He just lets it happen.

"Why, ladies and gentlemen, did not Paul Russell warn Mr. Garfield? There could be only two reasons: either Paul Russell was not honest enough to warn him, perhaps because he did not entirely reject the idea of committing the crime himself, or else the proposition was never made at all. In either case, Paul Russell did not act honestly. That is a fact, you see, an obvious fact, and it does not require any argument by me to make you see it."

Glancing back at the crowd, Bob Day noticed them looking at Russell, and he followed their eyes and saw Russell sitting and listening to his argument. For a moment their eyes met. Russell was angry, of course, and it showed on his face. I looked at him, and then I looked back at Day. The young lawyer was staring coldly at Russell, and I think I saw something which I may have imagined. Bob Day's eyes seemed to betray just a trace of elation. He was personally convinced, I am certain, of the innocence of Ruth Gibson, and consequently Russell was for him the villain in the case. I think he was glad to see Russell sitting there, hearing himself cut up. Day returned to the attack.

"The case for the prosecution rests on the word of Paul Russell. You are asked to take his word and therefore to believe that Roger Louis and Ruth Gibson and David MacKay and Dean Drayer are all lying. The case for the state rests on your taking his word against the word of others. But Paul Russell lies, ladies and gentlemen; under oath he lies. Besides the lie I have already pointed out—a lie which must be a lie because it cannot be anything else, either a lie to Mr. Garfield or a lie to us—besides that, he lied in his testimony at least one other time where his own words catch him. He told you under oath, ladies and gentlemen, that he could open the safe in the store. Under cross-examination he was compelled to admit that he could not open it, could not open it since a few days after the robbery, when Mr. Garfield changed the combination and did not give him the new combination. I will not comment on Mr. Garfield's changing the combination so Russell could not open the safe any more. I think the fact that he did it and when he did it is comment enough in itself. But I ask you to recall, if you will, the squirming and twisting Paul Russell did when he was questioned about this subject. He tried every way to evade it. He lied about it, never suspecting that his cross-examiner might know that the combination had been changed. It made him look good when he was allowed to open the safe. It showed how Mr. Garfield trusted him. But Mr. Garfield changed the combination. That made Paul Russell look bad. So he just overlooked that when he testified. He said he could open the safe, could still open it even today. That was not the truth. He squirmed when the lie was pointed out. He squirmed and became angry and indignant. But all of that could not conceal the fact that he had been caught in another lie.

"The prosecutor admits, ladies and gentlemen, that his case rests on the testimony of Paul Russell, and he suggests that it is uncharitable of us to attack him. I will not attack him any further. I have given you his motive for lying, and I have shown you two important lies he told. Those two lies are shown directly from his own testimony. If you point out the number of times when his testimony conflicts with that of other witnesses, then you see dozens of lies. I return, ladies and gentlemen, to my original point: the case for the state depends on your taking the word of Paul Russell against the word of others. His own testimony, within itself, without reference to the testimony of others, brands him with the mark of dishonesty and lies.

"Ladies and gentlemen, my associate in this case, Mr. Mac-Inroth, will conclude the argument for the defense."

It had been MacInroth's notion to use Bob Day, the young man, for the attack on Paul Russell, in the anticipation the jury might take it better coming from him. The consensus of the old hands around the courthouse was that Bob Day had make a good argument, had done a good job. When he sat down Ruth Gibson spoke to him and thanked him.

"Ladies and gentlemen of the jury," said John Kimball Mac-Inroth, and the jurors stirred in their places as if preparing themselves for oratory. MacInroth stepped from behind the defense table and stood without notes in the middle of the floor. "I thank my colleague, Mr. Day, for clarifying the issues in this case. I thank the prosecuting attorney, Mr. Baumgardner, too, for he also in his argument has pointed up the essential issue. You take the word of Paul Russell and you send two young people off to prison. That's a pretty heavy reliance to place on the word of Paul Russell. You saw the jail. This young woman, this girl, has been locked up in there for five months on the say-so of Paul Russell. We are giving serious consideration to locking her up for a good many years on the word of Paul Russell. And Roger Louis. We are asked to place a lot of confidence in the word of Paul Russell. A lot of confidence.

"There are lots and lots of things we could talk about, ladies and gentlemen. Lots and lots of things. But my associate and I decided we would confine our comment to the essential things in the case and not take up your time talking about all of the extraneous things which have gotten themselves into the evidence one way or another."

In this little town MacInroth is much admired for his courtroom oratory. The record of his words demonstrates his style. He opens his coat, puts his hands in his pockets, and wanders while he talks. Most of the time he is smiling, and he leans forward and looks out at the jury from beneath his brows. He suggests to the jury that he and they have a little joke together about how simple this case is and how amusing is the confusion other people have about it.

He spent some time rebutting the prosecutor's comments on the testimony of MacKay and Drayer, as of course he was compelled to do. There was nothing original in his remarks about the selective memory, any more than there had been in Baumgardner's. The situation is a cliché, and the arguments about it inevitably are too.

He asked the jury not to be prejudiced against Ruth Gibson because of the discussion of her morals, which he said had taken entirely too much time. He asked them not to be too much impressed with his client's bad check, because, as he said, Louis had redeemed the check and a bounced check differs from an armed robbery.

He returned toward the end of his argument to the principal theme of the defense—that the prosecution rested entirely on the word of Paul Russell. He asserted again that Russell was not a reliable witness and again he emphasized the enormity of the sentence the judge would pass if the jury convicted the pair solely on the word of Russell.

Then MacInroth passed on to a favorite theme of his and, in fact, of all defense lawyers:

"There comes a point, ladies and gentlemen, there comes a point in the trial of a case when the jury begins, I suppose, to wonder if anyone is ever going to say anything about justice. That, after all, is what we are here to see done: justice. Justice is your responsibility, your responsibility as a jury. You look at these two young people, and you must decide if you are going to condemn them to years of being locked away in cages because Paul Russell says you should. Would that be justice?

"Justice is represented in this courtroom also, ladies and gentlemen, by one of the basic principles of our American liberties. That basic principle is that no person is to be considered guilty until proven guilty beyond any reasonable doubt. Presumption of innocence, ladies and gentlemen. We are presumed innocent until proven guilty. Proved guilty beyond any reasonable doubt. The state must prove its case, ladies and gentlemen, beyond any reasonable doubt. If, after you have heard all the evidence and all the argument, there remains in your minds any reasonable doubt of the guilt of these two accused young people, then it is your duty to return a verdict of not guilty. The court will charge you about this and will explain in detail what reasonable doubt is. But remember, it is not for the defendants to prove they are innocent; it is for the state to prove them guilty, and that beyond any reasonable doubt.

"Ladies and gentlemen, the state has not proved these two young people guilty. A very large doubt remains. In fact, to the contrary, the defense has proved them innocent. And if you will keep your attention fixed on the essential facts of this case, I have no doubt as to what your verdict will be."

MacInroth moved closer to the jury, and his voice dropped. "Lastly, ladies and gentlemen, I want to say something to you about your responsibility and mine. We are not trying a capital case, ladies and gentlemen. The very lives of these two young people are not at stake. But if they are convicted they will be sent to prison for very long terms. Armed robbery is a serious crime, and the law provides a severe punishment. If you convict them, they will spend the remainder of their young years in prison. They will not be young people any longer when they come out. They will be much older and embittered. In a sense they will be destroyed. Their fate lies in the hands of us who plead their case and you who will decide. It is a heavy responsibility. Jury duty is one of the heaviest responsibilities citizenship imposes. It is to be approached reverently and with a sense of the awesome responsibility which it entails. Considering what will happen to these young people if you convict them, you would not want to convict them on the basis of a mere suspicion of guilt. Nor on the basis of disapproval of some of their past conduct. Nor on the word of a young man who has a motive to lie and who did lie to you as a witness. Nor without being fully and sincerely convinced, beyond any reasonable doubt, that the evidence requires conviction. If you make a mistake, they will suffer for years for that mistake, and perhaps we will too, we who tried them.

"We do not ask, ladies and gentlemen, that you acquit the guilty. We do not ask that you do an injustice to the state any more than to the accused. We do not ask you to act out of fear of your responsibility nor out of sympathy for the defendants. We ask only that you direct your attention to the evidence and to its essentials and that you do not return a verdict of guilty unless that evidence convinces you beyond a reasonable doubt that these two young people committed this crime.

"We ask for justice only, and fairness. Because we know that we have nothing to fear from your just verdict. We know your sense of justice and fairness will bring a verdict of not guilty.

"Lastly, ladies and gentlemen, we ask you to accept our thanks for your service in this most difficult job."

MacInroth returned to his table and sat down, and with an air of finality he tucked his note pad into his briefcase. It had been a typical MacInroth performance.

Joe Baumgardner rose then to conclude the argument for the prosecution. He had promised the jury he would have something to say about the testimony of the defendants, and he now fulfilled that promise by opening a cutting attack on their veracity.

"Ruth Gibson," he said. "Ruth Gibson—she is the one who doesn't lie, you remember—maybe she doesn't lie, but she says some very funny things.

"She says, for example, that she had no specific plans for going away, no specific plans, just a vague sort of general yearning to go away. So she says. But when I mentioned the name Sally Druro to her, then she admitted to a very specific plan. She denied any specific plan, in other words, until she found out that I knew about her plan. Then she admitted it. But her attorney says she doesn't lie.

"She says it was all talk, just talk. Part of that talk was a statement to Sally Druro that she would in a couple of weeks have enough money to buy a car and go to California. When she told Sally that, she didn't have any money. Where did she plan to get it?"

Joe Baumgardner grinned and shrugged, and showed the jury his upturned empty hands.

"This is Ruth Gibson we are talking about, remember, the one whose word is so much better than Paul Russell's. She is the one who doesn't lie, you remember. But she does say some peculiar things. She says she was in love with Paul Russell, so she let him have intercourse with her, and then she fell out of love with him pretty quickly and right into love with Roger Louis so she could let him do the same. She fought with Paul Russell because he wanted to have relations with her, and so she broke up with him and picked up another fellow and let him have what she fought with Paul about. She doesn't lie maybe, but she says some funny things.

"She testified that in May she was in love with Roger Louis. She also testified that she was planning to go to California and didn't tell Roger about that trip. I don't know how girls in love act, exactly. But I think that's a funny way for a girl in love with a fellow to treat him. She planned to go and never come back, but she didn't tell the man she loved. If it's true, it's a funny thing.

"Ladies and gentlemen, seriously, you heard the testimony of Ruth Gibson. She made a very good witness for herself. She is an intelligent girl. But she was not telling the truth. She plotted this robbery, recruited Louis to carry it out, sat in the car and waited while he did, and then she got caught practically red-handed, so she made up a fantastic story to cover herself. But it isn't the truth. On the whole it is fantastic, and at places here and there she was caught in the lie.

"Roger Louis," said Baumgardner, and he paused and grinned. "Well, Roger Louis. What can you say about him? He needed money, oh, how he needed it! He needed it so bad he wrote a bad check. He was going to lose his job and wouldn't have any wages for anyone to attach. He's a drinker, is Roger, and a hell-raiser, and when he needs money he's not above stealing it. He wrote the bad check. He joined in this fantastic story. He admits it is ridiculous. But in one thing Roger is fortunate. He has friends. He has friends who will lie for him. Not very good liars, not good enough to be convincing, but loyal enough to try.

"Ladies and gentlemen," said Baumgardner, adopting a more businesslike tone, "the case for the state does not rest on the word of Paul Russell alone. If it did I still think it would be strong enough to convict. But it does not, in spite of the defense's assertion that it does. It rests only partly on that. Besides the testimony of Paul Russell the state has shown you the motive for this crime, the pressing need which both defendants felt for money. Besides the eyewitness testimony of Paul Russell and the motives for the crime, the state has shown you the conduct of the defendants when they were caught. They ran, and in running they practically confessed their guilt. They made statements to the men who caught them, statements which no innocent person would make. The characters of both of them have been shown, and in each case you have seen a young person much in need of honesty and morality. Lastly, you have heard them lie under oath.

"Ladies and gentlemen, the defense asks only that you be fair. The state asks no more. The state does not seek the conviction of innocent people. If you are not truly convinced by the evidence, then acquit them, and the state will be satisfied. The state asks only that you arrive at your verdict after a careful consideration of the evidence. I am aware of your responsibility and of mine. My conscience will not rest easy with innocent people in prison through my prosecution, and I am not asking you to convict innocent people. On the other hand, we also owe a responsibility to society to convict the guilty when they are brought before us and not to let them run free to injure others, and that too is part of justice. That too is part of justice.

"Once again, ladies and gentlemen, we thank you."

Judge Kemp looked up at the clock and said, "The court will be in recess until one o'clock. The jury is admonished once again not to discuss the case with anyone and not to form an opinion until the case is concluded."

I have read of great trials when the lawyers were given a week to prepare their final arguments. I have read the fine arguments made by those lawyers who had a week after the case was finished to return to their offices and work on their speeches to their juries. I wonder how those lawyers would perform if they had to practice in a little county court like ours and if, like Joe Baumgardner, John MacInroth, and Bob Day, they had half an hour after the last witness testified in which to prepare. I do wonder. I can think of many other things they might have said. I know they can too. I wonder, however, if justice is not better served the way we do it. Our jury would retire to consider the case a few hours after hearing the last witness. Could they do as well after a week had passed? I doubt it.

It is perhaps a sort of rough and ready justice we dispense in the small-town courts of our rural counties. I think the way we try cases takes emphasis away from the lawyers and their arguments. Consequently, the evidence does not have to compete so much for the attention of the jury. And that is proper justice, for our courts should not give the judgment to the side which is best represented but to the side which has the evidence and therefore the facts in its favor.

XIII

When the court convened again at one o'clock, Judge Henry Kemp began his charge to the jury. It was a written charge, and Henry read it to them. When he was finished he would give them the pages from which he had read, and they would take those pages with them to the jury room for later reference. The charge contained the law the jury was to follow in arriving at its verdict.

The public seems never to understand this phase of trial practice. The jury by itself tries the facts. In this case, for example, the jury had before it two conflicting stories as to what happened at a given place at a given time. The jury and the jury alone must decide the facts, must in this case decide what had happened on that May morning. But having decided that, the jury must also decide what legal consequences follow from those facts before it can render a verdict. The charge to the jury is its instructions about the law.

The charge took almost half an hour, and it covered many points. Touching on some of the more important points, I may say that the judge first explained to the jurors that it was their duty to decide the case on the basis of the evidence presented. He defined the crime of armed robbery by telling the jury that to find the defendants guilty of armed robbery it must find that the defendants had, while armed with a pistol, knife, or other dangerous weapon, stolen something of value from the person of another by force or violence or by putting that other person in fear. He defined the crimes of larceny and assault, which were lesser included offenses, and of which under Ohio law the jury might find the defendants guilty instead of guilty of the major crime with which they were charged. He spoke of aiding and abetting, or of being an accessory to a crime, which was of course what Ruth Gibson was actually charged with. He talked about various kinds of evidence. He talked about character and the proof of it and about the weight the jury was to give character evidence in arriving at its verdict. He talked about alibi; it was, he said, a respectable defense which the defendants were entitled to assert, as good in law as any other, as the phrase is. He charged them that they were not to concern themselves with what the penalty might be, since that was a matter for the court alone to decide. He charged them about the presumption of innocence.

He defined reasonable doubt: "It is not a mere possible doubt, because everything relating to human affairs or depending upon moral evidence is open to some possible or imaginary doubt. It is that state of the case which, after the entire comparison and consideration of all the evidence, leaves the minds of the jurors in that condition that they cannot say they feel an abiding conviction to a moral certainty of the truth of the charge."

It was a good, competent charge, and none of the lawyers offered any objection to it.

Concluding, the judge told the jury, "When you retire to deliberate upon your verdict, you will take with you the exhibits which have been offered into evidence. You will also take with you written forms of verdicts, containing the different verdicts you might reach. The first thing you should do is elect one of your number to act as foreman or forelady to preside over your deliberations. When you have reached a verdict, by unanimous agreement as you have been instructed, your foreman should sign that form of verdict which corresponds to the verdict on which you have agreed. You should then knock on the door and notify the bailiff you have reached a verdict. The bailiff will be near your door at all times during your deliberations, and you may communicate only with him. You may, if you find it necessary, return to the courtroom and hear any portion of the trial record read to you by the reporter."

The judge stepped down from the bench and handed the typed pages of the charge and the verdict forms to Mrs. Teitelbaum, the juror nearest to him. Quentin, the bailiff, gathered up from the reporter's desk the bank ledger sheet and Ruth Gibson's little pair of shorts, which were the two exhibits in evidence, and handed them to Mr. Cleveland. Quentin then hurried around to the back of the jury box and opened the door to the jury room. The jurors, each one casting a final glance at Roger Louis and Ruth Gibson, walked through the door and out of the courtroom.

The time was 1:25.

Many writers have commented about the emotions people feel while juries are out, and I will try not to contribute to the quantity. Such writing is sentimental and dramatic, and it tries to convey the tension and the agony, and most of it is true. I suppose other experiences are worse, but I have not experienced them. I have experienced this, as a lawyer and a judge, though never as a defendant, and I can testify that agony and torture are proper words which do not exaggerate. The unpredictability and the irrationality of mankind go with a jury into the jury room, and no matter how the trial has gone you cannot feel confident about the outcome.

The penalty for armed robbery in Ohio is a term of imprisonment of not less than ten nor more than twenty-five years. With credit for good behavior, the first parole hearing could come up in about six years. So the very least which these defendants were facing was more than six years in prison.

Roger Louis rose without speaking a word to MacInroth and walked back to talk to his father and uncle. He sat down with them, and they conversed in low tones, looking up occasionally at MacInroth and probably criticizing his efforts. Shaking her head and apparently fearing the worst, Ruth Gibson spoke quietly with Bob Day.

Judge Kemp came over and sat down beside me. Bill Mullen had left the courtroom sometime before. Baumgardner and Mac-Inroth began to talk together, and MacInroth walked over to sit on the edge of the prosecutor's table. Most of the spectators in the courtroom kept their seats. A few left the room, only to return quickly. Lawyers know from experience that if a jury does not return in twenty minutes it will not return in an hour, and they are apt to wait twenty minutes and then go out for coffee. We followed that rule. The courtroom was quiet; no one spoke loudly. Quentin was the only comfortable person in the room. With his arms folded, he relaxed in a chair in front of the jury room. He would be the first to speak to the jury when the signal came, and he enjoyed his moment.

"What do you think?" Henry Kemp asked me.

"I used to guess them, Henry, but I was wrong so often that I gave it up. What do you think?"

"I think they are going to convict them. I'm not sure the burden of proof has been met, I'm not convinced beyond a reasonable doubt myself, but I almost am, and I think they will be."

"Well, just to make it interesting, I'll bet you a dollar," I said.

"That's a bet," Henry agreed. "Does that bet represent your opinion of the case or just a guess?"

"It just represents my obstinacy," I told him. "If you had said you thought they will be acquitted, I would have bet they would be convicted."

"Juries always frighten me," said Henry, looking toward the closed door of the jury room. "I always wonder if they are doing what they are supposed to be doing in there. I wonder some-times—I can't help it—if maybe they're not in there playing cards."

"Well, we'll never know. We can't know. We're not supposed to know."

"That's what we tell ourselves. Sometimes I wonder if the jury system isn't just an evasion of responsibility. We get twelve peo-ple together and lock them up together in a little room in secret, and by and by they come out and announce what they decided in secret, and we profess some mystic sort of confidence that whatever they decide must be right. We won't look beyond that. We say that they are, after all, the jury, so whatever they do must be right. We just close the question, like we close the door to the jury room."

"The only real justification for it, Henry," I said, "is that this method is superior to any other method which the ingenuity of mankind has thus far been able to conceive. It isn't perfect by a long shot, but have you got any better ideas?"

"Not at the moment," said Henry.

"That's the way with a lot of our arrangements, isn't it?" I went on, glad of the chance to lecture. "That's the way with a lot of our institutions, isn't it? Are we kidding ourselves that we have found the perfect way to organize a society or a government? Some of us kid ourselves that way. But isn't the fact actually that we are only doing the best we can and probably better than anybody has ever done before, even if it's still not ideal nor even near it?"

"There's nothing sacred in any of it, huh?"

"Not in my opinion. We should be careful, tampering with things that are working well. I'm conservative enough to think that. But we shouldn't be afraid to change arrangements if we really find a better way to arrange them."

"Well, getting back to our jury, do you suppose they really understand the case?"

"Maybe they understand it as well as we do. Tell me, can you say to an abiding moral certainty that you know what happened on the morning of May twentieth?"

"No, I can't. And I doubt they can, either. And that being the case, they should acquit, but I still don't think they will."

"I remember a wonderful charge I once heard a judge give a jury," I said. "He was explaining burden of proof, and he said, 'If upon consideration of all the evidence in this case you are unable to figure out what happened, then your verdict should be for the defendant.' I like that. I suppose, if we used it much, most cases would be won by defendants, but, after all, that's the law, isn't it?—if the state or the plaintiff fails to prove its case so the jury knows what happened with some degree of certainty, then the defendant should win."

"If you don't understand the case your verdict should be for the defendant," Henry chuckled. "Well, there's a lot of truth in that. Do you think I would dare use it?"

I shrugged. I dislike ending an amusing speculation by inquiring if I can really act on it. "Probably it's too easy an out," I said. "Juries would like to get off that easy."

"The way it is, they have to struggle and come forth with a verdict."

"Yes. Well, there's one thing I'm sure about, anyway. I'll bet I can tell you who they'll elect as foreman. Ed Jocelyn. Everybody except Schwallie and Paccinelli will go for that. A leader. A pillar of the community."

"Well, it's an appropriate choice," said Henry.

"And an empty honor."

Bill Mullen came in. His paper had gone to press without the opportunity to report the verdict. "How long would you guess they'll take?" he asked us.

"A couple of hours, anyway," said Henry.

"Yes, if not more," I agreed. "If they do a conscientious job they'll need that long to consider the case."

"I wouldn't mind if they were out overnight," said Bill.

"I remember," I said, "a jury I had one time that sat in the jury room for two hours after they reached a verdict and played cards and chatted. They reached their verdict in about ten minutes, but thought it seemed flippant to come out so soon."

"How did you find out?" Bill asked.

"One of the jurors complained about it to me later. She wanted to get on home, but she couldn't leave until the others agreed."

"What should they do in there, really?" Bill asked. "You tell them to elect a foreman and deliberate and reach a verdict, but you don't tell them how."

"No, we don't tell them how," Henry said. "They should review the evidence and then take a vote and then argue until they come to an agreement."

"I wouldn't make a good juror," Bill said. "Once I made up my mind about the case I wouldn't change it if I was the only one holding out."

"Then you'd make a very good juror," I contradicted him.

"Well," said Henry, "if some of them didn't give up their convictions and compromise, there would be a lot of hung juries."

"That's okay with me," I said. "In a criminal case the prosecution is supposed to convince twelve people, and if it only convinces eleven, it should get a hung jury."

"Well, you're an old libertarian," laughed Henry. "I wonder how anybody ever was convicted in your court."

"Nevertheless," I insisted, "I don't think jurors should compromise. That's not their function."

"This is lawyers' talk," said Bill. "I'm not with you entirely."

"Well," I said, "if people wanted their cases compromised they would compromise them themselves and be better satisfied with the compromise. They want juries to decide between them. One way or the other. And individual jurors should not compromise to get out of the jury room, either. That's betraying their obligation."

"I don't think you get much of that in cases like this," said Henry. "They can see it's important. But in your civil cases for money there's a tendency to want to get home for supper. I think they start flipping coins about a quarter till five."

"Yes, in your civil cases they usually think they have more important things to do than sit around here and settle the petty disputes between a pair of petty people," I said.

"In a case like this I'd think they'd be overwhelmed by the responsibility," said Bill. "I know I would."

"Yes, there's a lot at stake," said Henry, and so saying, he walked out of the courtroom.

I myself needed to visit the men's room so I took my leave of Bill Mullen and wandered out into the courthouse. I was gone about ten minutes, stopping in at one or two offices to chat awhile with my friends there. When I returned, the scene had not changed. Everyone was still waiting. Henry Kemp had returned and was sitting again with Bill Mullen. Joe Baumgardner had joined them.

"Judge, we were about to walk over to Billy's for a cup of coffee," said Joe. "Can we induce you to join us?"

"You think your jury is going to be out a while?" I asked.

"Yes, quite a while."

"The longer they're out, the more likely they will acquit," I said.

"I wouldn't be surprised if they do that," said Joe.

"I wouldn't be surprised at anything," said Bill Mullen.

"Maybe," said Joe, "the two gentlemen for the defense would like to join us too. Would you ask them, Bill?"

Bill Mullen nodded and went over to the defense table and spoke with John MacInroth and Bob Day. They were glad to leave the courtroom, and Mike Bradstreet, who was sitting in the jury box and talking to Quentin, took Ruth Gibson in custody. She would wait out the verdict in her cell.

Henry Kemp declined our invitation to join us, but the rest of us—Joe Baumgardner and John MacInroth and Bob Day and Bill Mullen and I—went to Billy's. Billy's—Reitlinger's Restaurant—is a big place, equipped to serve dozens of people. The bar is long with plenty of stools, and there are booths along the opposite wall, and tables, and a back room with more booths and tables. Billy was presiding behind his bar when we came in, and of course he came out and welcomed us with some show and offered us drinks on the house. The rest took coffee, but I was glad to have a Scotch and water, and Billy made it a double. We sat in a booth and drew up a chair to the end of it, and Billy drew up a second chair and joined us.

"Tonight," said Billy Reitlinger, "if that jury is honest and smart, there will be a celebration at Billy's in honor of my innocent girl. You are all invited. Even you, Joe Baumgardner, in spite of all the unkind things you said about her. I know you were just doing a job and you don't really think she did it."

"I'll take you up on that," said Joe. "If you have that celebration I'll be needing a drink."

"We'll be having it, and I'll buy a drink," said John MacInroth.

"I'm glad you're that confident," said Bob Day wryly.

"Well, when you defend the innocent you can afford to be confident," said John with a smile and a shrug.

"Sure," said Billy Reitlinger. "He believes in his people. That's a lesson, young man. I'm no lawyer, of course, and Billy's not supposed to be too smart, but I know a thing or two, and I've seen a lot of lawyers in this town in my time. Let me tell you one thing: the lawyer who believes in his clients is the best lawyer. You've got to believe you're doing right. If you have any doubts about the case yourself, how can you do a good job convincing somebody else that you're right? The jury can tell. They can tell whether you believe in your case. That's why Ruthie's gonna win; Joe Baumgardner doesn't really believe she's guilty, and the jury can tell. Right, Joe?"

Joe Baumgardner only smiled and did not answer.

"Come on now, Joe," Billy said. "The trial's over. You don't really think she's guilty, do you?"

"Billy, what I think makes no difference," said Joe. "You know that. It's what the jury thinks that counts."

"I thought I detected a lot of conviction in your efforts to win a conviction," observed Bill Mullen.

"Well," said Joe Baumgardner, "the defense puts a lot of first-class legal skill to work for its side of the case. Can I do less than my best for the people I represent? John says he believes his client is innocent. Well, John always says that. I don't say I believe everyone I prosecute is guilty. But what I believe has nothing to do with it."

"That's right," I said.

"Well," said Bob Day, "you wouldn't prosecute someone you believed was innocent."

"I wouldn't seek the indictment," said Joe. "But if there's reasonable cause to think a person has committed a crime, then it's my duty to prosecute. I don't decide whether people are innocent or guilty. That's for the jury."

"Always the jury," said Billy Reitlinger. "It's something how we can sit here and be jolly while the jury is over there deciding whether to send poor Ruthie away for ten years. Where is she now, anyway?"

"Back in the jail," said Bob Day. "She said she'd just as soon wait it out there."

"It's gotten to be sort of a home to her," said Billy.

"Some people can be comfortable anywhere," said Bill Mullen.

"She's not comfortable," said Billy Reitlinger. "You seen that place?"

I changed the subject.

"Do you gentlemen plan to appeal if your jury convicts?" I asked the two defense lawyers.

"We got some pretty raw rulings," complained John MacInroth.

"Even I won't deny that the judge gave me some rulings I didn't expect," said Joe Baumgardner.

"I don't know," said Bob Day. "I've thought about it. I didn't like some of the rulings, but I have to admit the judge ran a reasonably good trial."

"What do you think, Judge?" Bill Mullen asked me.

"Well, I don't comment on Judge Kemp's conduct of his court. I make that a rule."

"There were a couple of places," said John MacInroth, "where he was just plain wrong."

"Yes, but I don't know that it hurt us really," said Bob Day.

"I didn't like that business about Roger hauling down that girl's pants," said John. "I don't think that was necessary."

"Oh, Jesus!" laughed Joe Baumgardner. "What would you have done if you had been me?"

"I'd have got it in if it was the last thing I ever did," said John grimly.

"Say, they're a hell of a nice lot of people, those Louises," said Billy. "Aren't they?"

"I'll be damned if they're not," said MacInroth.

"That nasty little son of a bitch turns my stomach," said Bob Day.

"Yes, he turns mine too," said John. "I'd like to see him sent up for something, sometime when I'm not defending him."

"I thought you said the nasty little son of a bitch was innocent," said Joe Baumgardner.

"The nasty little son of a bitch *is* innocent," laughed John.

"All your clients are innocent, aren't they, John?" I said. "You've even got some innocent clients in the penitentiary."

"Well, now, Judge," said John. "After all your years of experience you're not going to assert that all the people in the penitentiary are *ipso facto* guilty, are you?"

"I'm not even going to assert that all the people I sentenced were guilty. Only that juries found them guilty."

"*Ipso facto*," said Billy. "Why can't you speak English?"

277

"That's lawyers," said Bill Mullen. "They take pride in being incomprehensible."

We sat in Billy's and talked past three o'clock, and still no word came from the courthouse. When we returned, the courtroom was nearly deserted. Quentin still sat stoically before the door of the jury room. The Louises sat in the rear of the room and held their private conversation. Ever frugal, Quentin had turned out the lights, and the courtroom looked unusually dim and shabby. John MacInroth and Bob Day decided to go to their offices, leaving word in the clerk's office to call them if there was any knock on the jury room door. Bill Mullen and Joe Baumgardner wandered away somewhere. I sat down in my office for a moment and then went over to where Quentin sat. Through the door I could hear the muted and confused sound of voices. The jury was deliberating.

"They did some hollering in there a while ago," laughed Quentin. "Somebody got mad."

I only nodded acknowledgment of his words. I went back to my office and sat down at my desk. In a little while Joe Baumgardner came in.

"Judge," he said, "you knew my old German grandfather. What would he think of me being in the business of sending people to the penitentiary?"

"Your grandfather thought the law was a very fine profession," I said.

Joe Baumgardner acknowledged my evasion of his question with a significant smile, and he lowered himself into the chair beside my desk. "What do you think?" he asked, inclining his head in the direction of the jury room.

"I have a dollar bet that they'll acquit," I said. "But not because I really think so."

"No, they'll convict them," he said.

"Do I detect that you are less than enthusiastic about that?" I asked.

"Oh, I suppose they're guilty, as far as that's concerned," he said.

"Well, then?"

He shrugged. "But I'm not sure."

"As you yourself said, you don't have to be sure. The jury—"

He interrupted me. "The jury doesn't settle the thing," he said. "Not for me. Not for you, I should think. We know too much about juries."

"It bothers you then when someone is convicted and you're not personally convinced of the guilt?"

"Yes," he said. "I don't make a good prosecutor. I could find myself throwing cases if I weren't careful. What's a prosecutor's duty, anyway? Should I pursue convictions with vigor and enthusiasm? Or just present the facts and let it go at that? Do I have to stand up in argument and call the defendants liars and all that? Should I do that or not?"

"Well," I said, "I suppose as long as defending lawyers are vigorous in defending—"

"Prosecutors have to be vigorous in prosecuting," he finished my sentence for me. "Our minds run in the same channels, Judge. That's just the way I've reasoned. But maybe that's just an evasion. That means I let the defense decide how the trial will be run."

"Well, I don't think you did or said anything improper in prosecuting this case," I told him, because I understood at last that he had come in to solicit that assurance.

"Well, it sort of got out of control. I didn't mean to get on the girl so much. I had intended to concentrate on the boy."

"Well," I said, "she turned out to be the principal personality. Roger Louis is a cipher."

"It's funny," he said, "how life is for some people. They are not socially desirable people. I mean they are marginal people, living on the edge between normal existences and the life of real felons. They might have tended back toward normality. There really isn't anything wrong with her, especially. It all comes from her background. But suddenly they do this thing. Now they're beyond redemption."

"You're a little ahead of yourself," I said. "What do you think will happen to them if this jury acquits them? That's still a possibility, you know."

"Yes," he agreed—almost hopefully, I thought. "But if they are acquitted they've still been pushed a good deal in the wrong direction. If they are innocent, they will be bitter. I would be, wouldn't you? This town will never leave them alone now."

"Oh, let's stop a minute on that point," I said. "People of their class aren't going to be particularly disturbed about what the town thinks. Louis especially. Opinion won't mean anything to him. To her—well, maybe."

"If she gets acquitted, and if she's smart, she'll go out to California and find Sally Druro," said Joe. "If she hasn't the money, I'll contribute to a fund. I'll put in fifty dollars. Will you match it?"

"Yes," I said. "Billy will put in a hundred, and Bob Day and John. We can send her to California."

Joe nodded. Then his eyes dropped, and he shrugged and said, "But they'll convict her."

"Well, I wouldn't be too sure," I said. "They've been out a long time." It was approaching four o'clock.

"Not so long," he said.

"Did anybody," I asked, "ever make a search of Paul Russell's apartment for the loot?"

"No. If he did take it, he would be too smart to hide it there. We've watched him pretty closely. I went all back through his record, in school, the service, and so on; he doesn't have a black mark against him anywhere."

Bill Mullen came to the door and asked if he might come in, and we said he might. "I've been wandering around and got to thinking," he said. "If she was in jail and he wasn't, how did they get their stories together? I mean about why they ran from the sheriff and all?"

"Well," said Joe Baumgardner, "he was in jail for a few days, and you know how they can talk back and forth up there."

"It's not very private, though. Someone ought to have heard them," Bill Mullen said.

"Well, there's another way they could have matched stories," I said. "Through their lawyers."

"Yes," said Joe, "and the fact that they didn't bring up this point suggests that's just how it was done."

"Well, is that ethical?" Bill Mullen asked. "Do you lawyers do those things?"

"It could be ethical or unethical," I said. "It depends on how it was done. If they manufactured a story out of whole cloth, then it would be unethical. But if they helped their clients iron out discrepancies, it would not be."

"They didn't make it up," said Joe positively. "If they had they would have made up a better story than that. The two defendants made it up."

"I suppose," said Bill, "that Day and MacInroth were stuck with a lot of things they would rather have not had in the trial."

"Well," said Joe, "you have to take your cases as they come. You can't make them up like a playwright."

I agreed and added that it probably was too bad, too. We talked a few minutes, and then my two visitors decided to return to the courtroom. I was alone, and I got up, stood at the window, and looked down on the town.

The wind was still blowing cold out of the north, out of Canada. The sky was still gray, as it had been all day, and the stores along the streets were lighted, and their neon signs were lighted. At four o'clock the high school children, just released from school, were running along the streets. They dashed exuberantly toward their various destinations, which in most cases was a stop for a Coke on the way home. Unmindful of the traffic, shouting and laughing, they dodged in and out among the pedestrians and across the streets. People stood talking on the corners of the streets, and occasionally I would see one glance toward the courthouse. The subject of their talk was plain. On the green metal benches on the courthouse lawn, some of the people who had been in the courtroom during the trial sat ignoring the cold wind. Their backs were toward me; they all hunched because of the temperature, and they looked heavy and solid. They were the community, the judges. They were dissatisfied, I knew. They had come to the trial expecting to find out whether Roger Louis and Ruth Gibson were guilty or innocent, and though the trial had ended they still did not know. They were suspicious. They would believe for a long time that Joe Baumgardner had held something back. They would believe the same of John MacInroth and Bob Day. They would be critical of Judge Kemp. They would be critical of the jury. The verdict would not settle their questions.

From my window I could see DeWitt's Jewelry Store, and I could see Paul Russell standing in the door looking toward the courthouse. He was ruined. Whatever the jury did, he was ruined. He was not just sensitive to public opinion; he was hypersensitive. For a time he could toy with the flavor of being a suspected felon and the air of mystery about it, and it might impress a few girls; but in the end, sneak theft and perjury are not romantic crimes, and there is no comfort in being suspected. As the defense had suggested, he wanted a conviction. It would relieve him somewhat. He stood in the door, and he would come across the street at the first suggestion that the jury was coming back. The newspaper was on the street. It carried Bill Mullen's story, grotesquely severed because the paper could not wait for the end. That I suppose is the tragedy of the journalism business.

It was my town, imperfect but determined not to be concerned with its imperfections; resistant to progress but not immune; poor, as all these hill towns are poor, a good place to live in but a bad place to make a living. And I could write a book. Behind those walls, behind the façades of tall hedges, is enough scandal for a book that would sell like the Bible. But it would be betrayal, and, after all, the community has been good to me, even though it suspected, I think, what contempt I have occasionally felt for it. Besides, they could tell some stories about me if they wanted to.

My paper was of course on my desk. I sat and read it, and after a while I called Mary and told her not to come for me. I had decided to stay until the jury came out, if it took half the night.

I said that we lawyers have a rule that if a jury does not come out in twenty minutes it will not come out in an hour. We have another: if it is still closeted at five o'clock it is apt to be hung. In these little towns we do not let juries deliberate for weeks on end. I knew that Judge Henry Kemp would dismiss this jury if it did not reach a verdict by midnight, which is what I would have done too. But along about five they begin to think of dinner and of spending the evening at home, and the pressure to agree mounts. Nevertheless, five came and went. The jury knocked on the door and asked for coffee and sandwiches, and when they did Joe Baumgardner, Bill Mullen, and I went out to eat. We stayed after dinner and had a couple of drinks, and we did not arrive back at the courtroom until almost seven.

Judge Kemp came in. He had been home for dinner with his wife. John MacInroth and Bob Day were sitting at their table again, and the Louises were holding another conspiratorial conference in the back of the courtroom. Bill Mullen said he would not be surprised if they pulled guns and ran out if the verdict was against the boy. Quentin had switched the lights on because it was dark outside. He still sat before the door to the jury room, and we wondered if he had eaten. Some fifty spectators were present now, most of them people who had not been in during the trial. Paul Russell was there, accompanied by a pretty blond girl. The jury had been out more than five hours.

At 7:13 one of the jurors rapped on the jury room door. Quentin opened it a crack, received the word from inside, and closed the door again. He crossed the courtroom to Judge Kemp, who was sitting beside me.

"They're ready," he said.

"Get someone to bring the girl in," said the judge.

Henry Kemp looked at me, and without a word he rose and went to his place on the bench. Bill Mullen moved up to take his seat, but he said nothing either. Even to us, disinterested and uninvolved as we were, it was an emotional moment, and chatter seemed inappropriate. We had said all that needed to be said.

We waited for the girl. Several minutes elapsed before Chloe Adams brought her in. They came in through the door opposite my seat and crossed the front of the room to the defense table. Ruth Gibson was pale. Her lips were parted slightly, and her eyes were wide and stared straight before her. Chloe held her arm and guided her, as though she could not walk. I have never seen a human being so frightened. Only after she was seated did Roger Louis come forward and take his place beside MacInroth.

With everyone in place, Judge Kemp nodded to Quentin, and Quentin opened the door of the jury room. The jurors came out, with Ed Jocelyn, who had been elected foreman, emerging first. He was carrying the verdict forms. He was followed by William Cleveland, who carried the bank statement and Ruth Gibson's shorts. After them each of the jurors followed, looking tired and, under the court's scrutiny, embarrassed. A courtroom legend holds that a jury which convicts will not look at the defendant. We watched their eyes, but we could tell nothing. Some looked. Some didn't. Ed Jocelyn took the seat nearest the judge, the one Mrs. Teitelbaum had had. He looked confident that he was doing right. He would not have done whatever he had done without first assuring himself of that. Cleveland had done a job. He was not a sensitive man. He was not upset. Joe Paccinelli was grim. To him it had been extremely unpleasant, and he was not satisfied with the processes of justice, into which he now had a startling insight. Linda Tubman and her new-found lover, Taylor, looked nervous and unhappy. The rest of them could not be read.

Ed Jocelyn handed the verdict forms to Quentin, and Quentin passed them to the judge. The judge looked at them and separated the signed forms which represented the decision from the unsigned ones. He handed the two signed forms to Tate Gimball, clerk of the court of common pleas. Tate, a rotund old man, looked at each of them and then began to read. His voice was not large, and people strained to hear.

"The State of Ohio, Marshall County, ss: In the Court of Common Pleas. State of Ohio versus Roger Larimer Louis. Indictment for Armed Robbery. Case Number one-eight-one, two-five-six. We the jury, being duly impaneled and sworn, find the defendant Roger Larimer Louis guilty of armed robbery. Signed, Edward A. Jocelyn, Foreman of the Jury."

Roger Louis turned and glanced at his father and uncle, and then he turned back to watch the clerk read the other verdict. His expression did not change. Ruth Gibson gasped and her hands shot up and covered her face.

"The State of Ohio, Marshall County, ss: In the Court of Common Pleas. State of Ohio versus Ruth Elaine Gibson. Indictment for Armed Robbery. Case Number one-eight-one, two-five-seven. We the jury, being duly impaneled and sworn, find the defendant Ruth Elaine Gibson guilty of armed robbery. Signed, Edward A. Jocelyn, Foreman of the Jury."

She dropped her head to the table; it struck with an audible thud. Her high-pitched uncontrolled sobbing overwhelmed every other sound in the courtroom, and people with much to say kept their silence and looked at her. Bob Day placed his hand on her back and gently patted it, and Chloe Adams rose and stood behind her and touched her head. Roger Louis leaned forward and, looking past his attorney, watched Ruth. He blinked his eyes as if so much emotion puzzled him.

In the jury box Linda Tubman put her head down in her hands and began to cry also, shaking and sobbing, and Taylor put his arm around her and said something to her. Mrs. Teitelbaum put her handkerchief to her eyes and wiped away tears. The rest of them, in their various ways, looked miserable. Except Cleveland, and he was not a sensitive man.

For several minutes Judge Kemp did not try to restore order. He could not have silenced Ruth Gibson anyway. People began to talk, and some began to move out through the rear doors to carry the news. Paul Russell did not look happy, and the blond girl clutched at his arm and spoke to him. Billy Reitlinger wept; the tears ran down his cheeks, and he made no effort to wipe them. Joe Baumgardner, alone at his table, looked down and waited for the judge to close the session.

"All right. All right," said the judge finally.

The crowd quieted, but Ruth Gibson continued to cry. Judge Kemp waited for another moment, and then went on to speak above her as best he could.

"Bond of the defendant Roger Louis is not continued," said the judge. "His bondsmen are discharged, and he is remanded into the custody of the sheriff. Motions will be heard at eleven-thirty Monday morning. Sentencing will be at nine o'clock on Thursday a week from today. Members of the jury, you are discharged until nine Monday morning when you must report again. I thank you for your service. The court stands adjourned."

It was over. Well, not quite over, because Henry still had to sentence Ruth and Roger. Nevertheless, it was over for most purposes, and would quickly lose its interest as a topic of conversation. For a day or two hardly anything else was discussed in Alexandria—or in all of Marshall County, I imagine—but Friday night and Saturday afternoon brought the weekend football games, and the next weekend would mark the high school homecoming game. Interest shifted, and the town found other subjects for its gossip.

On Monday morning the attorneys appeared in a deserted

courtroom and made their motions for judgment notwithstanding the verdict and for a new trial, and everyone understood that the judge would overrule them. And he did.

On Thursday the case came to sentencing. That drew a few people. Roger Louis, who had now been in jail a week, saw no point in putting on a coat and tie for this occasion; he came in a checkered shirt, open at the neck, and a pair of old blue jeans. Ruth Gibson had by now regained her color and her ability to walk unaided, but you could see her pain.

The judge asked each of them if he had anything to say as to why sentence should not be passed. This the law requires.

"I didn't do it," said Roger Louis. It was an inaudible mumble, and the judge had to ask him what he had said. "I didn't do it," repeated Louis in a louder and an impatient tone.

"Well, the jury thought you did," said Judge Kemp.

"Yeah, I guess so," agreed Louis.

"How about you, Ruth?" asked the Judge.

"It wasn't fair," said Ruth in a strident voice that might have been offensive if it were not so obvious that she was also struggling to hold down thick sobs that were accumulating high in her throat. "It just wasn't fair."

Judge Kemp waited a moment and then asked, "Is that all you want to say, either of you?"

"Is it going to make any difference?" Ruth said.

"Probably not," Judge Kemp said, "but you have a right to speak if you want to, and I'll listen."

"Well, it wasn't fair," Ruth said again resentfully. "There just wasn't anything right or fair about it."

Judge Kemp took a breath, and then in a quiet voice, without the slightest trace of satisfaction in his job, he said, "It will be the sentence of the court that Roger Louis be imprisoned in the Ohio Penitentiary for not less than ten nor more than twenty-five years and that Ruth Gibson be imprisoned in the Ohio Reformatory for Women for not less than ten nor more than twenty-five years. You must pay the costs of prosecution."

I saw the two of them for the last time on the following Monday morning. About eight o'clock, Bill Mullen looked in at my door and told me the sheriff was taking Roger Louis and Ruth Gibson off to prison. I went out in the hall to see them go. They were in the sheriff's office, and in a moment they came out. George, the sheriff, led the little procession, which would go down the steps and out to a car he had warmed up and waiting. Behind George walked Roger, looking down at the floor. He was wearing a heavy leather belt, and at the front of this belt was a thick brass ring. Through the ring was the chain of Roger's handcuffs, so that the young man could not raise his hands away from his waist. As he passed by Bill Mullen and me, Roger Louis looked up at us through narrowed eyes, and then quickly looked away again. Ruth was behind Roger. She was wearing the same little white blouse and short blue skirt and white slippers she had worn the last day of the trial. She had on handcuffs, without the belt, and she was embarrassed to be seen in them and so held her hands and arms folded against her waist to conceal the manacles as much as she could. Chloe Adams came last, and Ruth stopped and asked Chloe to walk beside her, and Chloe moved up. As they passed by us Ruth glanced at us impersonally and without apparently recognizing either of us. They turned and started down the steps. About halfway down, Ruth hesitated momentarily and turned her head and looked back at us as if she wanted to say something, but Chloe took her arm and led her on. At the bottom of the steps they passed through the door and out of my sight. I have never seen either Roger Louis or Ruth Gibson again, and I do not expect to.

There was an appeal. The Louises would not pay for one. The Gibsons, however, somehow managed to borrow enough to pay a reasonable fee for that purpose. They took it to Columbus and hired a lawyer there, who called on Bob Day to write him a long letter and point out the places in the record where in Bob's opinion Judge Kemp had made errors. Bob did it, somewhat ruefully. The court of appeals did not reverse the conviction. It found errors but said they were not important enough to warrant a new trial.

More than a year has passed now since the trial. The two convicts remain in their prisons. Joe Baumgardner is dead. A heart attack carried him away in January, and we lost a very fine man.

Paul Russell does not live in Alexandria anymore. He quit his job—the rumor persists, of course, that he was quietly fired—and he married the blond girl and moved to Charleston, West Virginia, where he works in a store. For the rest of us, life is not much different. Bob Day received two letters from Ruth Gibson after the court of appeals had refused to order a new trial for her. In the first she begged him to try to get her out, and he wrote back and said there was nothing more he could do for her. Several months later she wrote and thanked him for all he had done. She said they were teaching her cosmetology in the reformatory. He showed me the letters. And I of course still hold forth as always in my office in the courthouse. Some people say I will never die, and for all I can tell they could be right.

Some people still want to know whether Roger Louis and Ruth Gibson were really guilty or not. I don't know. I can only say they were convicted.